Mathematics for Key Stage Three

The topic-based tests in this book are a brilliant way to stay on top of the KS3 Maths skills you'll need throughout Years 7-9 (ages 11-14) — and each one will only take up 10 minutes of your life!

This is **Book Three**, which covers the **most challenging material** from KS3 Maths. It's perfect to use alongside Book Two, which covers the core KS3 content. If you're looking for a simpler introduction to KS3 Maths, try Book One!

10-Minute Tests

Book Three

Contents

Number

Ratio, Proportion and Rates of Change

Algebra

Geometry and Measures

Probability and Statistics

Published by CGP

Editors: Shaun Harrogate, Ceara Hayden, Caley Simpson

With thanks to Alastair Duncombe and Jonathan Wray for the proofreading.

ISBN: 978 1 78294 474 4

Printed by Elanders Ltd, Newcastle upon Tyne.
Clipart from Corel®
Based on the classic CGP style created by Richard Parsons

Number: Test 1

Give yourself **10 minutes** to do this test — there are **7 questions** to answer.

Quick-fire Questions

1. Which of these is <u>not</u> a square number?

A 16

B 50

C 100

(1 mark)

2. Which of these <u>is</u> a cube number?

A 64

B 100

C 9

(1 mark)

3. Zahra divides 1692 books equally amongst 12 identical bookcases.

Without using a calculator, work out how many books she puts on each bookcase.

....
(1 mark)

4. Without using a calculator, complete this factor tree to find the prime factorisation of 120.

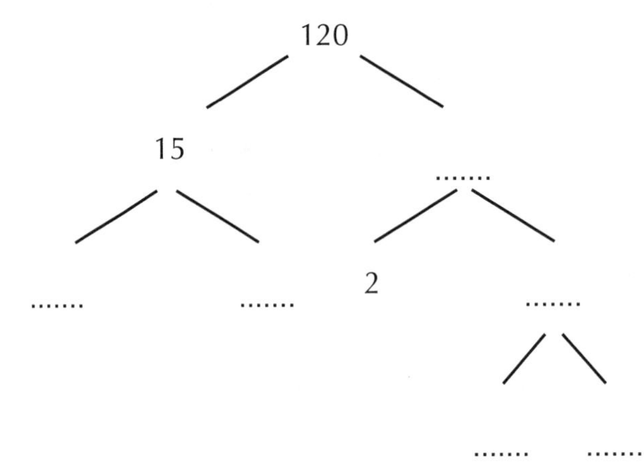

(2 marks)

5. **Chris, Teo and Harry walk to school. The distances they walk are shown below.**

Chris: $\frac{4}{15}$ km, Teo: $\frac{3}{5}$ km, Harry: $\frac{1}{3}$ km

Without using a calculator, put the boys in order based on how far they have to walk.

Longest distance .... , ... , ... Shortest distance

(2 marks)

6. **Simplify $2^5 \times 2^6$ without using a calculator.**

Give your answer as a power of 2.

....

(1 mark)

7. **Viv has a cube-shaped fish tank. It has a volume of 22 000 cm^3.**
Use the formula below to work out the side length of her fish tank.

$V = S^3$	where V = volume and S = side length

Give your answer to 2 decimal places.

.... cm

(2 marks)

Score: ___ / **10**

Number: Test 2

Give yourself **10 minutes** to do this test — there are **7 questions** to answer.

Quick-fire Questions 

1. **What is 0.72 as a percentage?**

   A 72%

   B 7.2%

   C 0.72%

   (1 mark)

2. **What is $\frac{3}{5}$ as a decimal?**

   A 0.3

   B 0.6

   C 0.35

   (1 mark)

3. **Which of the numbers below are prime?**

1	17	63	39	71	115

....

(1 mark)

4. **Jodie is comparing how much sugar there is in her two favourite cereals.**

Steady Break	*Maple Rings*
Sugar per 42 g serving: 11 g	Sugar per 36 g serving: 8 g

Which cereal has the lowest percentage of sugar?

....

(2 marks)

5. Work out the lowest common multiple of 6, 8 and 12.

Do not use a calculator.

....
(2 marks)

6. Daniel can run 100 m in 14.39 seconds. He rounds his time to 2 significant figures.

What is his rounding error?

.... seconds
(1 mark)

7. Without using a calculator, evaluate the expression below when $p = 3$.

$$\frac{1^{18} \times (p^2)^3}{p^5 \times p^{-2}}$$

....
(2 marks)

Score: $\frac{}{10}$

Bonus Brainteaser

Using Daniel's time in Q6, what would his rounding error be if he rounded to 1 decimal place?

.... seconds

Number: Test 3

Give yourself **10 minutes** to do this test — there are **7 questions** to answer.

Quick-fire Questions

1. **What is 56% of 200?**

   A 28

   B 56

   C 112

   (1 mark)

2. **What is 300% of 60 g?**

   A 120 g

   B 180 g

   C 20 g

   (1 mark)

3. **Barretstown Secondary School has six classes of 28 students and nine classes of 17 students.**

   Without using a calculator, work out how many students there are in the whole school.

   ....

   (1 mark)

4. **Jakub eats $\frac{11}{20}$ of a 600 g pie.**

   Without using a calculator, work out how much pie Jakub eats.

.... g

(1 mark)

5. **Work out both square roots of the following numbers.**

289

....
(1 mark)

62.8849

....
(1 mark)

6. **Use this table to work out the value of $\frac{16\,807}{49}$. Do not use a calculator.**

7^1	7
7^2	49
7^3	343
7^4	2401
7^5	16 807

....
(1 mark)

7. **Ballymore has a population of 6.2×10^4 people.**
In Ballymore, there are 1.4×10^2 different newsagents.

Write down the population of Ballymore as an ordinary number.

....
(1 mark)

How many people are there per newsagent? Give your answer to the nearest whole number.

....
(2 marks)

Score: ___ / **10**

Number: Test 4

Give yourself **10 minutes** to do this test — there are **7 questions** to answer.

Quick-fire Questions

1. Which number below is rational?

A $\sqrt{5}$

B π

C $\frac{3}{4}$

(1 mark)

2. Which number below is not rational?

A $\frac{6}{17}$

B $\sqrt{2}$

C 8^2

(1 mark)

3. Round the following numbers as specified.

6.457 to 1 decimal place

....

(1 mark)

0.652365 to 2 significant figures

....

(1 mark)

4. Oscar wants to divide his 20 seeds equally into pots.

Fill in the table below to show all the ways he can do this.

Number of pots	Number of seeds per pot
1	20
	10

(1 mark)

5. **Niko bought three aubergines at £0.79 each, two parsnips at £0.47 each and four mangoes at £1.12 each.**

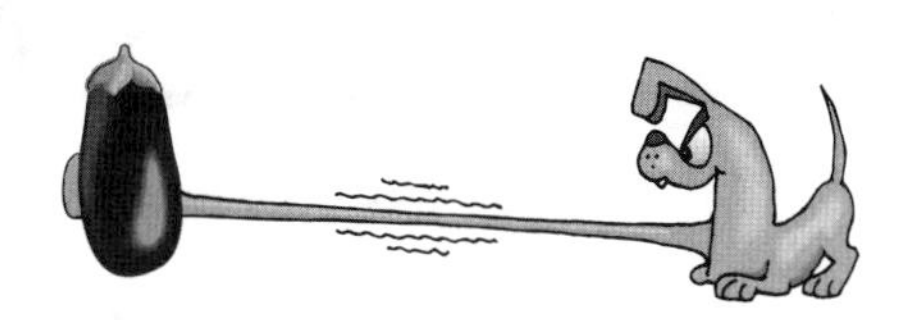

Without using a calculator, work out how much he spent in total.

£ ....
(2 marks)

6. **Complete this factor tree and use it to write 420 as a product of its prime factors.**

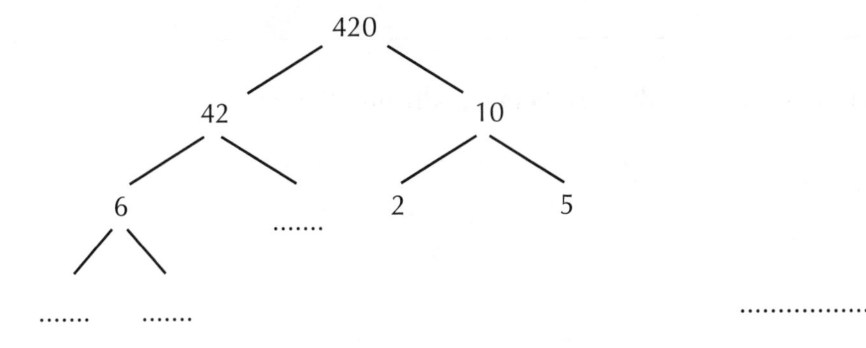

....
(1 mark)

7. **Shibu walked $6\frac{3}{4}$ miles one morning. He then walked $4\frac{5}{8}$ miles in the afternoon.**

Without using a calculator, work out how far Shibu walked in total.
Give your answer as a mixed number.

.... miles
(2 marks)

Score: $\frac{\quad}{10}$

Bonus Brainteaser

Shibu then swam $\frac{3}{5}$ of a mile each day for the next 8 days.
How many miles had he swum after 8 days?
Give your answer as a mixed number. .... miles

Number: Test 5

Give yourself **10 minutes** to do this test — there are **7 questions** to answer.

Quick-fire Questions 

1. **What is 0.793 rounded to 1 significant figure?**

   A 1.0

   B 0.8

   C 0.7

   (1 mark)

2. **What is 936 324 rounded to the nearest thousand?**

   A 936 000

   B 936 300

   C 940 000

   (1 mark)

3. **Toby finds 942 jewels in a cave. He divides them equally into 8 different bags.**

   Without using a calculator, work out how much jewels he has left over.

.... jewels
(1 mark)

4. **Find the highest common factor of 36, 63 and 108.**

   Do not use a calculator.

....
(2 marks)

5. **Work out these calculations without using a calculator.**

Give your answers as improper fractions in their simplest forms.

$\frac{8}{15} + \frac{3}{5}$

....

(1 mark)

$\frac{13}{10} - \frac{1}{4}$

....

(1 mark)

6. **Without using a calculator, write the number 973 600 in standard form.**

....

(1 mark)

7. **M. J. Guest Cheesemongers sells three different-sized cheeses. They've decided to offer either an extra 55 g of cheese or an extra 6% of cheese with every cheese bought.**

Which sizes of cheese would be better value if the customer asked for 55 g extra?

Small	Medium	Large
834 g	906 g	963 g

....

(2 marks)

Score: — / **10**

Number: Test 6

Give yourself **10 minutes** to do this test — there are **7 questions** to answer.

Quick-fire Questions

1. $12 + 3 \times 8 \div 2 = ?$

A 18

B 24

C 60

(1 mark)

2. $(18 + 6) \div 3 \times 2 = ?$

A 16

B 4

C 22

(1 mark)

3. Write <, > or = in each box to make the statements correct. Do not use a calculator.

$\frac{1}{10}$ ☐ 0.1

$\frac{1}{2}$ ☐ 0.2

0.7 ☐ $\frac{1}{7}$

3.5 ☐ $\frac{7}{2}$

(2 marks)

4. Ruth goes to Tai Chi every four days. Chris goes to Tai Chi every five days.

If they both go to Tai Chi today, how many days will it be before they next go to Tai Chi together? Do not use a calculator.

....

(1 mark)

5. **Work out the following without using a calculator.**

Calculate $-\frac{2}{3} \times \frac{4}{5}$.

....
(1 mark)

Calculate $2\frac{1}{2} \div \frac{3}{8}$, giving your answer as a mixed number in its simplest form.

....
(1 mark)

6. **The formula $V = S^3$ is used to find the volume of a cube. V = volume and S = side length.**

If S = 17 cm, find V.

.... cm^3
(1 mark)

7. **Estimate the answer to this calculation by rounding each number to 1 significant figure.**

$$\frac{58.7 - 32.4}{2.85 \times 1.9}$$

....
(2 marks)

Score: ___ / **10**

Bonus Brainteaser

Use the formula in Q6 to find the side length of a cube with volume 24 587 m^3. Give your answer to 3 significant figures.

.... m

Number: Test 7

Give yourself **10 minutes** to do this test — there are **8 questions** to answer.

Quick-fire Questions

1. What is $\frac{2}{5}$ as a percentage?

A 40%

B 32%

C 16%

(1 mark)

2. What is 0.84 as a percentage?

A 80.4%

B 8.4%

C 84%

(1 mark)

3. Write down all the prime numbers between 16 and 34.

....

(1 mark)

4. Liz has $\frac{3}{5}$ of her birthday cake left.
She divides it equally between herself and three friends.

Without using a calculator, work out the fraction of the cake each person gets.

....

(2 marks)

5. Evaluate $\sqrt[4]{6482}$ to 2 decimal places.

....

(1 mark)

6. **James believes that only three of the numbers below are real.**
Is he correct? Explain your answer.

π $\quad\sqrt{3}\quad$ 0.2 $\quad 34 \quad$ $\frac{1}{9}$

....

....

(1 mark)

7. **z = 213 to the nearest whole number.**

Find the upper and lower limits of the possible values of z.

Upper limit = ...

Lower limit = ...

(2 marks)

8. **Use the table below to show that 64 × 1024 = 65 536.**

4^1	4
4^2	16
4^3	64
4^4	256
4^5	1024
4^6	4096
4^7	16 384
4^8	65 536

....

....

(1 mark)

Score: ___ / **10**

Number: Test 8

Give yourself **10 minutes** to do this test — there are **7 questions** to answer.

Quick-fire Questions

1. **What is the lowest common multiple of 9 and 12?**

   A 72

   B 3

   C 36

   (1 mark)

2. **What is the highest common factor of 36 and 48?**

   A 6

   B 12

   C 18

   (1 mark)

3. **Without using a calculator, work out the calculation below.**

   $(-14) + (-27) - (-43)$

   ....

   (1 mark)

4. **Roz spends £34.64 on a new dress in a sale. She pays with a £50 note.**

   Without using a calculator, work out how much change she gets.

   £ ....

   (1 mark)

5. Without using a calculator, write the following numbers in order from smallest to largest.

0.22 $\frac{17}{100}$ 19% $\frac{4}{25}$ 0.18

.... , ... , ... , ... , ...
(2 marks)

6. Charlie's website gets 4650 hits a day, to the nearest ten.

Give the range of possible values for the actual number of hits, h, as an inequality.

....
(2 marks)

7. A snail moves at an average speed of 0.002 mph.

Write this speed in standard form without using a calculator.

.... mph
(1 mark)

Use the fact that $\frac{1}{500} = 0.002$ to write $\frac{1}{5000}$ in standard form without using a calculator.

....
(1 mark)

Score: — / **10**

 Ratio, Proportion and Rates of Change: Test 1

Give yourself **10 minutes** to do this test — there are **8 questions** to answer.

Quick-fire Questions

1. **What is 862 g in kg?**

   A 8.62 kg

   B 0.862 kg

   C 0.0862 kg

   (1 mark)

2. **1 inch ≈ 2.5 cm. Approximately how many inches are in 10 cm?**

   A 25 inches

   B 5 inches

   C 4 inches

   (1 mark)

3. **Without using a calculator, simplify this ratio as far as possible.**

   2.5 : 12.5

   ....

   (1 mark)

4. **8 farmers can plough a field in 1 day.**

   Assuming they all work at the same rate, how long does it take 4 farmers to plough the same field?

   .... days

   (1 mark)

5. **Richard is folding his shirts.**

   It takes him 15 minutes to fold 20 shirts.
   How long will it take him to fold 32 shirts?

   .... minutes

   (2 marks)

6. **20% VAT is added to the basic price of all bikes in a bike shop.**

The basic price of Katherine's bike was £480.
How much does she pay after VAT is added?

£ ....
(1 mark)

7. **Tim has made a model of a submarine using a scale of 1 : 150.**

His model is 7.2 cm wide.
What is the real-life width of the submarine in metres?

.... m
(2 marks)

8. **A statue has a mass of 8610 kg and a volume of 0.82 m^3.**

Calculate its density in kg/m^3.

.... kg/m^3
(1 mark)

Score: —— **10**

Ratio, Proportion and Rates of Change: Test 2

Give yourself **10 minutes** to do this test — there are **6 questions** to answer.

Quick-fire Questions

1. What is 24 : 4 in the ratio n : 1?

A 6 : 1

B 1 : 6

C 2.4 : 1

(1 mark)

2. Which ratio is the same as 1 : 5?

A 5 : 10

B 5 : 25

C 1 : 2.5

(1 mark)

3. A koala weighs 1 stone 11 pounds. How heavy is the koala in ounces? Use the conversion rates below to find your answer.

1 stone = 14 pounds
1 pound = 16 ounces

.... ounces
(2 marks)

4. Basil's shop sells jars of luxury pickles in three different sizes.

A small jar costs £1.20 and contains 10 pickles.

A medium jar costs £3.60 and contains 40 pickles.

A large jar costs £11.00 and contains 100 pickles.

Without using a calculator, work out which jar of luxury pickles is the best value for money.

....
(3 marks)

5. **Alan wants to open a new bank account that pays 3.5% simple interest each year.**

He decides to put £200 in and leave it untouched for 4 years.
How much interest will he have earned by the end of 4 years?

£ ....
(1 mark)

6. **A sailing boat is blown at 6 km/h by the wind for 3 hours and 30 minutes.**

How far, in km, does it travel in this time?

.... km
(1 mark)

The sailing boat travels another 5 miles before it reaches a boat house.
Given that 1 mile ≈ 1.6 km, work out the total distance, in km, travelled by the boat.

.... km
(1 mark)

Score: —/10

Bonus Brainteaser

Basil's medium jar of luxury pickles has a mass of 819 g and a volume of 780 cm³. Work out the density of the medium jar in kg/cm³.

.... kg/cm³

Ratio, Proportion and Rates of Change: Test 3

Give yourself **10 minutes** to do this test — there are **6 questions** to answer.

Quick-fire Questions

1. 4 bananas cost 80p.
How much do 6 bananas cost?

A £1.00

B £1.20

C £1.40

(1 mark)

2. If it takes 3 people 4 hours to paint one room, how long would it take 1 person to paint the same room?

A 6 hours

B 8 hours

C 12 hours

(1 mark)

3. Shehan is planning a walk in the countryside.
His map, shown below, has a scale of 1 cm = 2 km.

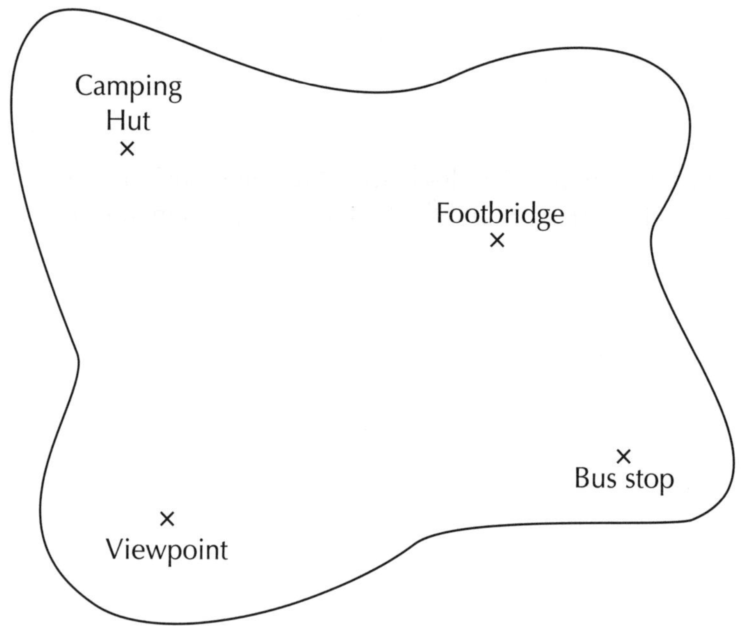

What is the real-life distance between the bus stop and the camping hut?

.... km

(1 mark)

Shehan walks in a straight line from the footbridge to the viewpoint.
After 9 km, he finds a bench. Mark the bench on the map.

(1 mark)

4. **Kate works out that the number of minutes she spends talking on her phone and the number of minutes she spends texting on her phone are in the ratio 6 : 27.**

For every minute she spends talking on her phone, how many minutes does she spend texting?

.... minutes
(1 mark)

5. **Jess has decided to cycle 18 km to work. She leaves her house at 7.00 am and gets to work at 7.45 am.**

Without using a calculator, find her average speed.

.... km/h
(2 marks)

6. **A farmer only has pygmy goats and miniature pigs on his farm. The ratio of pygmy goats to total animals on the farm is always 5 : 11.**

In winter, there are 55 animals in total on the farm. How many pygmy goats are there?

....
(1 mark)

In summer, there are 15 pygmy goats on the farm. How many miniature pigs are there?

....
(2 marks)

Score: **—/10**

Ratio, Proportion and Rates of Change: Test 4

Give yourself **10 minutes** to do this test — there are **7 questions** to answer.

Quick-fire Questions

1. A map has a scale 1 : 100. What real-life distance is represented by 4 cm on the map?

A 400 m

B 40 m

C 4 m

(1 mark)

2. Adam has 20 cm^2 of chocolate. How much is this in mm^2?

A 2000 mm^2

B 200 mm^2

C 0.2 mm^2

(1 mark)

3. Octavia buys a house for £150 000.

She sells it 5 years later for £187 500. What is her percentage profit?

.... %

(2 marks)

4. *x* is directly proportional to *y*.

Sketch a graph to show the relationship between *x* and *y* on the axes below.

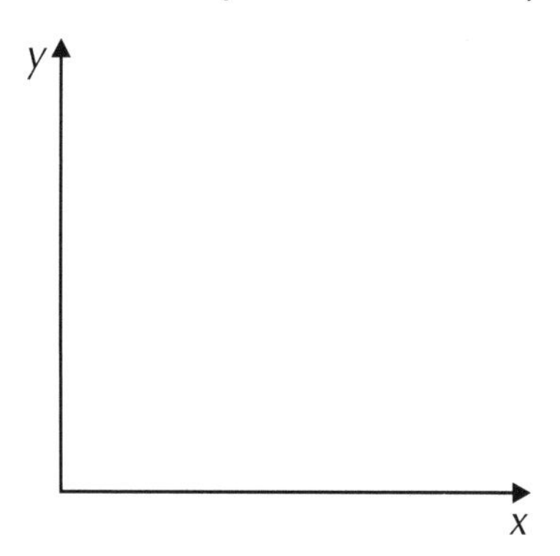

(1 mark)

5. **Ainsley uses 240 g of couscous in a recipe for 10 people.**

How much couscous will he need to feed 44 people? Give your answer in grams.

.... g
(2 marks)

6. **The value of Mike's laptop is inversely proportional to how many times he drops it on the floor. It was worth £150 after he'd dropped it four times.**

Write an equation to represent this inverse proportion in the form $L = \frac{k}{d}$,
where L is the value of his laptop and d is the number of times he drops it.

....
(2 marks)

7. **Steven buys a skateboard for 40% less than the original price. It costs him £39.**

How much would he have paid if he had bought it at the original price?

£ ....
(1 mark)

Score: — / **10**

Algebra: Test 1

Give yourself **10 minutes** to do this test — there are **7 questions** to answer.

Quick-fire Questions

1. Multiplying out the brackets in $3(8x + 5)$ gives...

A $38x + 35$

B $24x + 5$

C $24x + 15$

(1 mark)

2. Multiplying out the brackets in $8y(5x - 6y)$ gives...

A $40xy - 48y^2$

B $40xy - 48y$

C $40xy + 48y^2$

(1 mark)

3. $288 = 32n$

Without using a calculator, find the value of $16n$.

$16n$ = ...

(1 mark)

4. Use the grid below to answer this question.

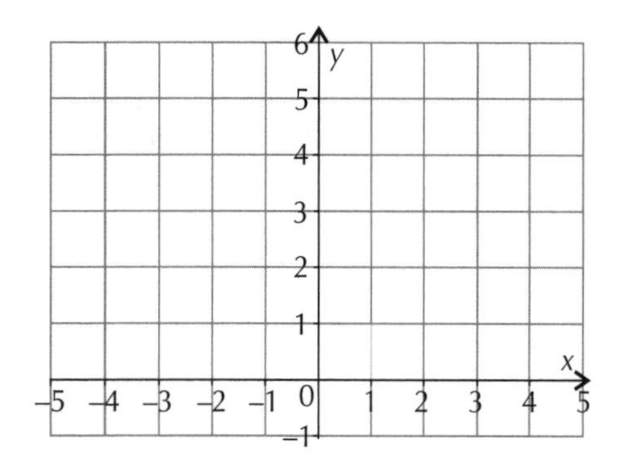

Plot the following points on the grid:

A (–1, 1) **B** (–3, 5) **C** (4, 0)

(1 mark)

Now find the coordinates of the midpoint of the line segment AB.

....

(1 mark)

5. Aoife is thinking of a number.
She says, "If you double my number, then add 5, the result is 15."

Let N be Aoife's number. Write an equation involving N.

....
(1 mark)

6. Four equations of straight line graphs are shown in the box on the right.

$2x + y = 7$	$3x + 8 = y$
$x + 2y = 7$	$3x - y = 8$

Which two lines go through the point (3, 1)?

.... and ....
(2 marks)

7. Eimear runs a cattery. The formula below is used to work out how much it costs (£C) to put a cat in her cattery for a given number of days (d).

$$C = 5 + 2d$$

Rearrange the formula to make d the subject.

....
(2 marks)

Score: $\frac{\quad}{10}$

Bonus Brainteaser

Use Eimear's formula in Q7 to work out how much it would cost to put a cat in her cattery for two weeks.

£ ....

Algebra: Test 2

Give yourself **10 minutes** to do this test — there are **7 questions** to answer.

Quick-fire Questions

1. **Which of these points has the coordinates (–2, 2)?**

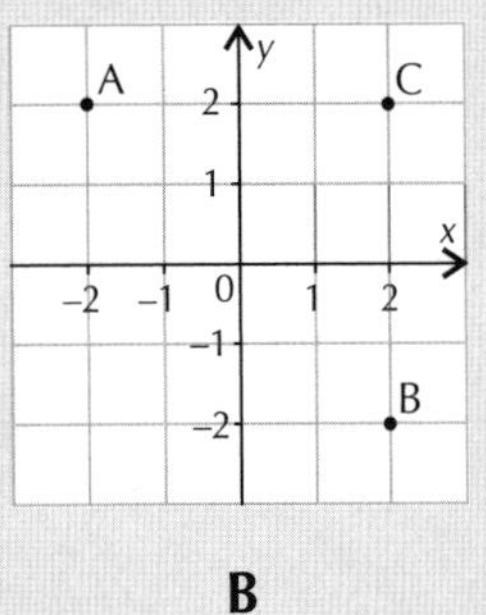

A **B** **C**

(1 mark)

2. **What is the equation of the line AB?**

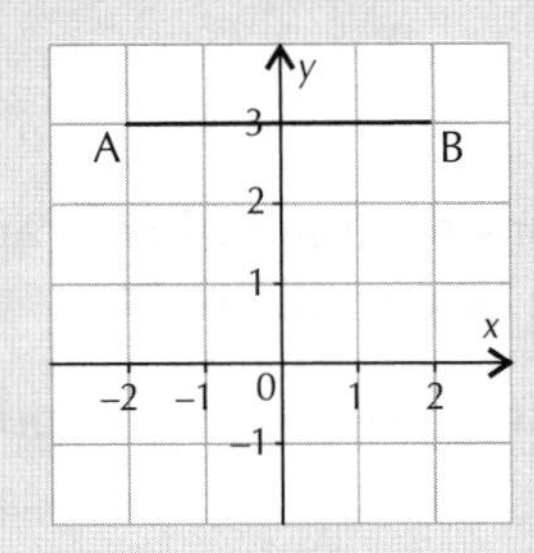

A $y = -3$ **B** $x = 3$ **C** $y = 3$

(1 mark)

3. **The *n*th term of a sequence is $10n + 7$.**

Find the first 5 terms of the sequence.

.... , ... , ... , ... , ...

(1 mark)

4. **This graph shows how much it costs to visit the fairground and go on some rides.**

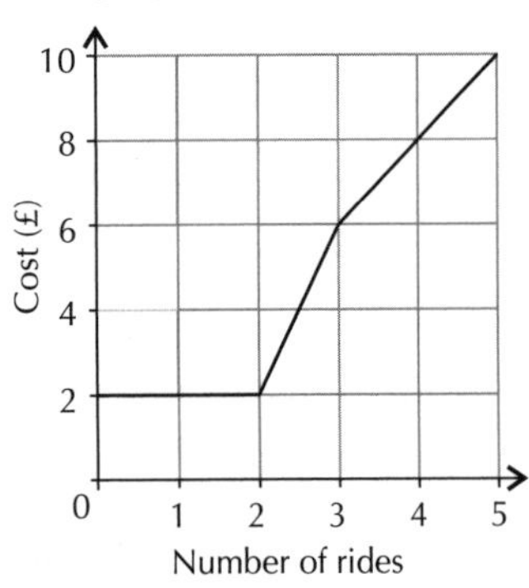

How much does it cost to go into the fairground and go on 4 rides?

£ ....

(1 mark)

5. **Expand and simplify this expression.**

$(x + 5)(x - 4)$

....

(1 mark)

6. **Solve the equation below for *x*.**

$\frac{x}{8} + 2 = -8$

$x =$ ....

(2 marks)

7. **Fully factorise the following expression.**

$12ab^2 - 9ab^3 + 24ab$

(3 marks)

Score: **/ 10**

Algebra: Test 3

Give yourself **10 minutes** to do this test — there are **6 questions** to answer.

Quick-fire Questions

1. **What is the next number in this sequence?**

   8, 5, 2, –1, ...

   A 2

   B –3

   C –4

   (1 mark)

2. **What is the next number in this sequence?**

   2, 4, 8, 16, ...

   A 24

   B 28

   C 32

   (1 mark)

3. **The formula for Trang's love potion is below.**

$$L = 60v + \frac{1}{2}e^2$$

Find L when $v = -0.1$ and $e = 8$.

L = ...

(1 mark)

4. **Look at the graph below.**

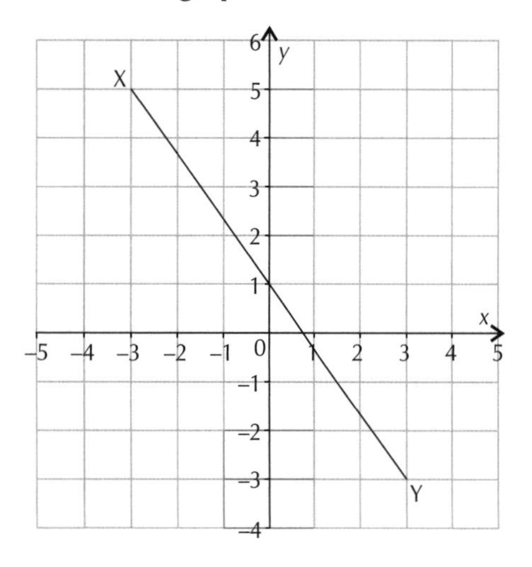

Find the coordinates of the midpoint of the line segment XY.

....

(1 mark)

Point W has the coordinates (–3, –1).

What are the coordinates of the midpoint of the line segment WY?

....

(1 mark)

5. **Cho has a paddling pool. Its area is shown by the equation below.**

Area = $8p - 5pq$

If the length of her pool is p, find an expression for the width of her pool.

....

(2 marks)

6. **The graph of the equation $y = 3x - 2$ is a straight line.**

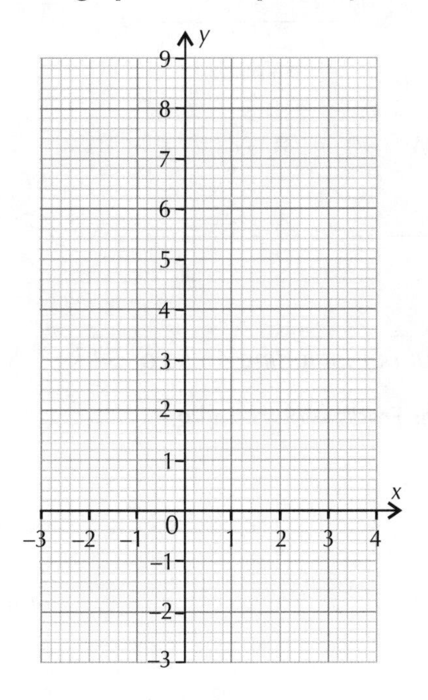

Complete the table of values for this equation. Plot the values on the axes and join them up with a straight line.

x	0	1	2	3
y				

(2 marks)

Now estimate the coordinates of the point where the line $y = 3x - 2$ intersects the x-axis. Give your answer to 1 decimal place.

....

(1 mark)

Score: —— / **10**

Bonus Brainteaser

On your graph for Q6, draw the line $y = 4 - 2x$. Now use the graph to solve the simultaneous equations $y = 3x - 2$ and $y = 4 - 2x$.

x = ... y = ...

Algebra: Test 4

Give yourself **10 minutes** to do this test — there are **7 questions** to answer.

Quick-fire Questions

1. This graph shows the cost of taking luggage on a plane. How much does it cost to take 8 kg of luggage?

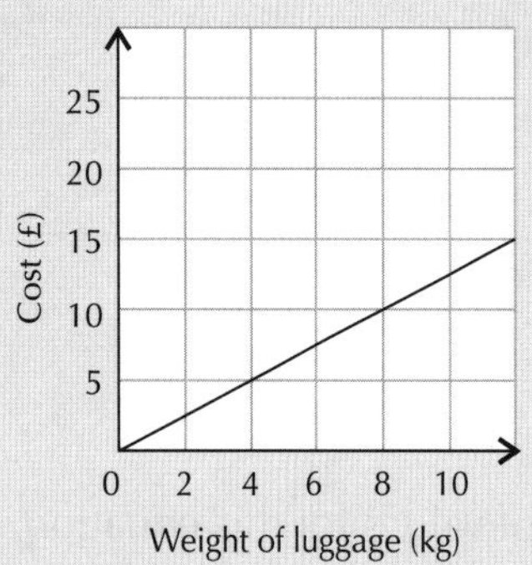

A £10 **B** £6 **C** £8

(1 mark)

2. This graph shows the exchange rate at a Post Office. How many pounds (£) would you get for €50?

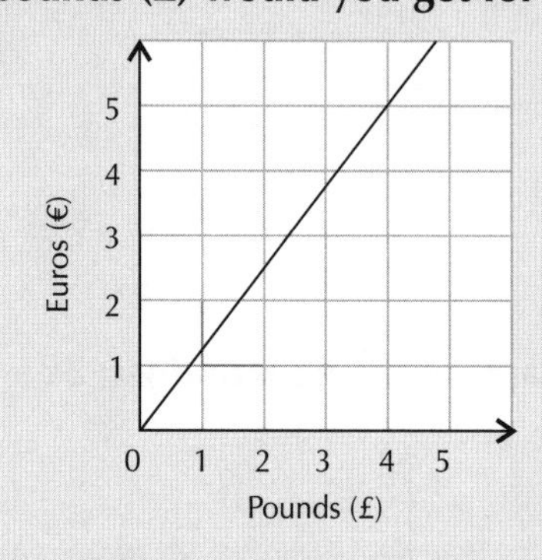

A £40 **B** £4 **C** £50

(1 mark)

3. George is trying to guess how much Fred weighs.

Fred says, "I weigh between 46 kg and 54 kg, but not including 46 kg or 54 kg."

Write an inequality to show this information. Use w for Fred's weight in kg.

....

(1 mark)

4. Solve the equation below to find x.

$5(3x - 9) = 5x + 15$

$x =$ ....

(2 marks)

5. Use this graph to solve the simultaneous equations below.

$y = 2x - 1$

$2y = -x + 8$

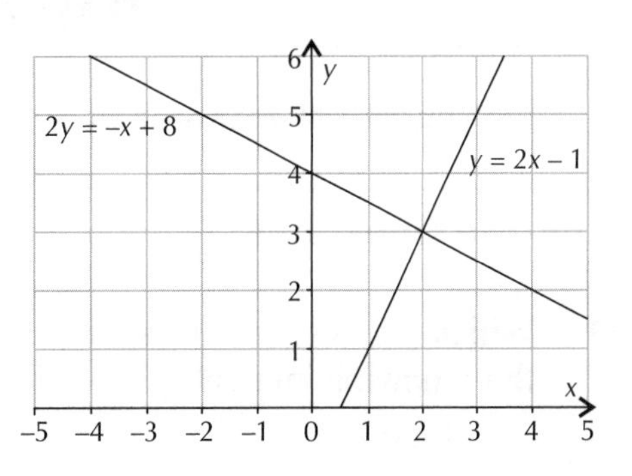

x = ... , y = ...

(1 mark)

6. Albus is a window cleaner. He charges a one-off fee for each house in addition to a charge per window. His rates are shown below.

One-off charge per house: £4
Charge per window: 50p

Let h be the number of houses and w be the total number of windows Albus cleans. Write an expression to show how much Albus earns from cleaning windows in pounds.

....

(1 mark)

7. Solve the equation below to find x.

$$\frac{x-9}{8} = \frac{x-6}{2}$$

x = ...

(3 marks)

Score: ___ / **10**

Algebra: Test 5

Give yourself **10 minutes** to do this test — there are **6 questions** to answer.

Quick-fire Questions

1. **Which integers are included in the following inequality?**

   $-3 < n \leq 2$

   A $-3, -2, -1, 0, 1, 2$

   B $-2, -1, 0, 1, 2$

   C $-3, -2, -1, 0, 1$

   (1 mark)

2. **Which inequality correctly summarises this group of integers?**

   65, 66, 67, 68, 69

   A $64 < x < 69$

   B $65 \leq x < 69$

   C $65 \leq x < 70$

   (1 mark)

3. **Points D, E and F have been plotted on the graph below.**

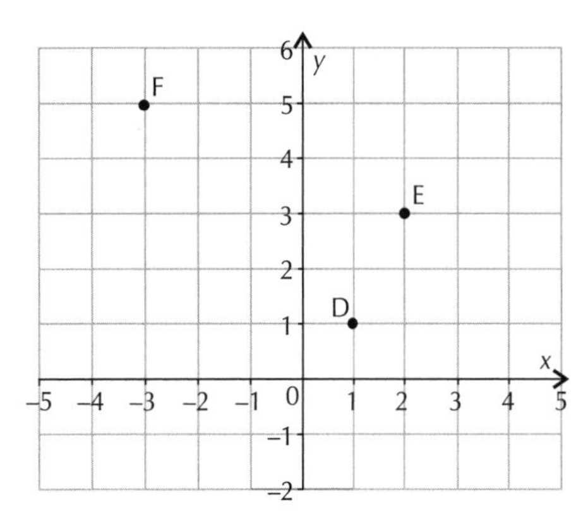

What is the gradient of the line DE?

....

(1 mark)

What is the gradient of the line DF?

....

(1 mark)

4. **Alice is making jam tarts for a picnic. To work out how many she needs to make, she starts with the number of guests going to the picnic, doubles it, then subtracts 2. She then squares the result.**

   If t represents the number of guests going to Alice's picnic, write an expression for the number of jam tarts she needs to make.

....

(1 mark)

5. **Here is a table of values for the equation $y = x^2 - 2x - 3$.**

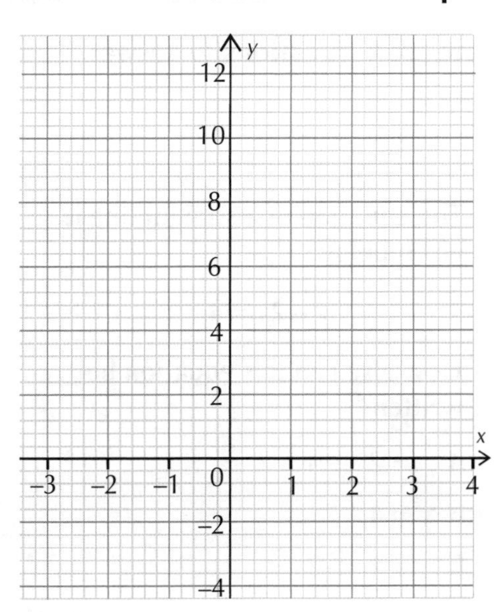

x	−3	−2	−1	0	1	2	3	4
y	12	5	0	−3	−4	−3	0	5

Use the table to draw the graph of $y = x^2 - 2x - 3$.

(1 mark)

Use the graph to estimate the solutions to the equation $x^2 - 2x - 3 = -2$ to 1 d.p.

$x =$ .... and $x =$ ....

(2 marks)

6. **Rearrange the formula $s = \frac{1}{2}(u + v)t$ to make t the subject.**

....

(2 marks)

Score: /10

Bonus Brainteaser

Rearrange the formula in Q6 to make v the subject.

....

Algebra: Test 6

Give yourself **10 minutes** to do this test — there are **6 questions** to answer.

Quick-fire Questions

1. **The points below show 3 vertices of a parallelogram. What are the coordinates of the fourth vertex?**

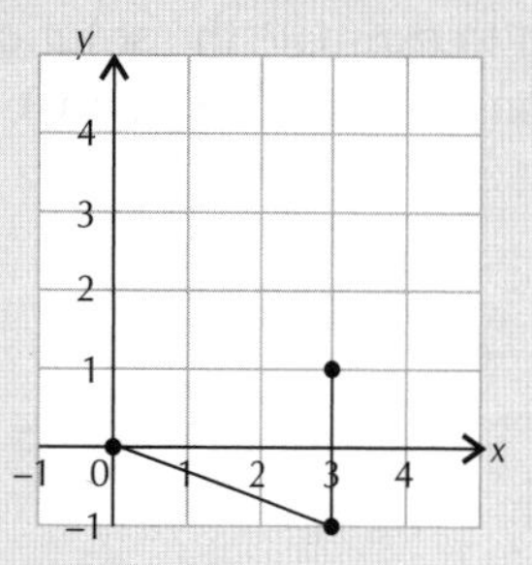

A (1, 2) **B** (2, 0) **C** (0, 2)

(1 mark)

2. **The equation of a straight line is given below:**

$$y - 2x = 4$$

How else can this equation be written?

A $y = 2x + 4$

B $y = 4 - 2x$

C $y - 4 = -2x$

(1 mark)

3. **Solve the following equation to find *h*.**

$4 - 6h = -14$

$h =$ ....

(1 mark)

4. **The gradient of the line joining the points (3*p*, 3) and (5*p*, 9) is 3.**

Find the value of p.

$p =$ ....

(2 marks)

5. **Below are the first three patterns of a sequence.**

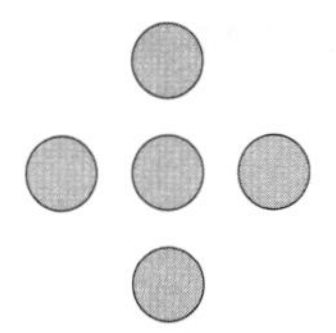

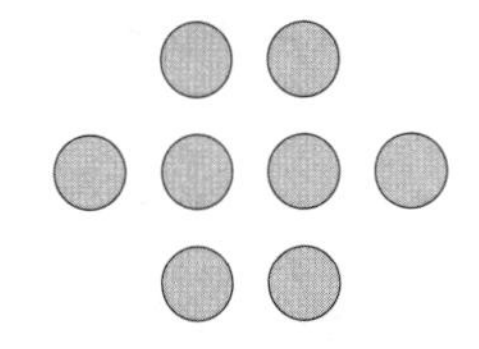

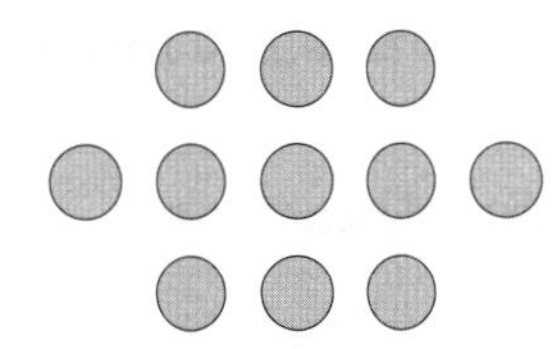

Draw the fourth pattern in the sequence.

(1 mark)

How many dots are in the nth pattern of this sequence?

....

(2 marks)

6. **The graph below shows a reciprocal graph.**

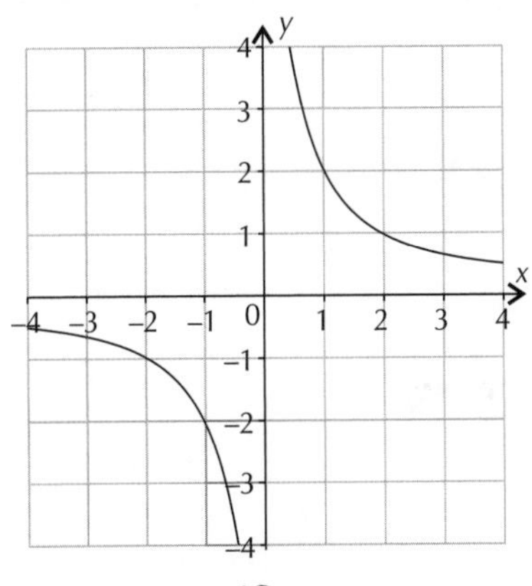

Use the graph to find the value of y when $x = 2$.

y = ...

(1 mark)

Use the graph to find the value of x when $y = -1$.

x = ...

(1 mark)

Score: __ / **10**

Algebra: Test 7

Give yourself **10 minutes** to do this test — there are **6 questions** to answer.

Quick-fire Questions

1. $9x^2 - 4x + 8x^2 - 4 + 9x + 6$ **simplified is...**

A $17x^2 + 5x + 2$

B $18x^2 + 4x + 2$

C $17x^2 + 9x + 6$

(1 mark)

2. $xy^2 + 5x + 8x + 5xy^2$ **simplified is...**

A $xy^2 + 13x + 5xy$

B $19x^2y^2$

C $6xy^2 + 13x$

(1 mark)

3. **The table of values for the graph $y = ax + b$ is given below.**

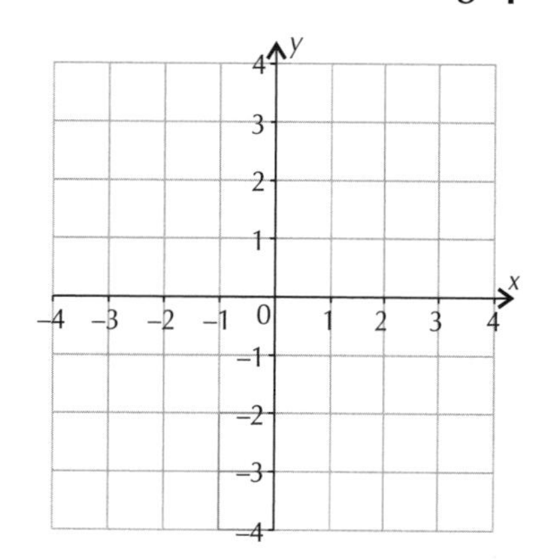

x	–1	0	1	2
y	3	1	–1	–3

Plot the points on the axes and join them up with a straight line.

(1 mark)

What are the values of a and b?

a = ... b = ...

(1 mark)

4. **Show the inequality $-4 < x \leq 1$ on the number line below.**

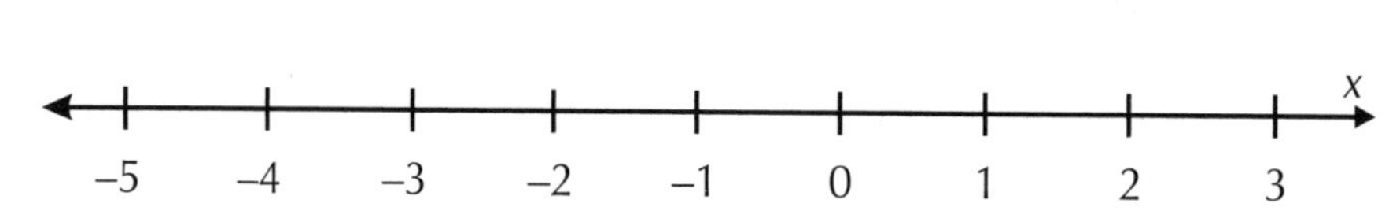

(1 mark)

5. **Edward has been on three different journeys.**
Match the distance-time graphs below to the right description.

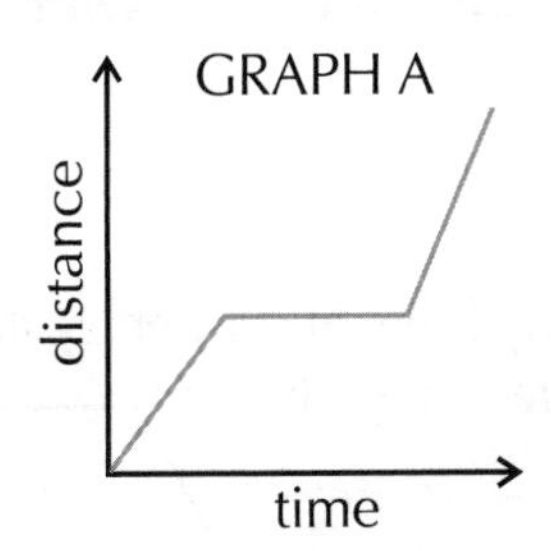

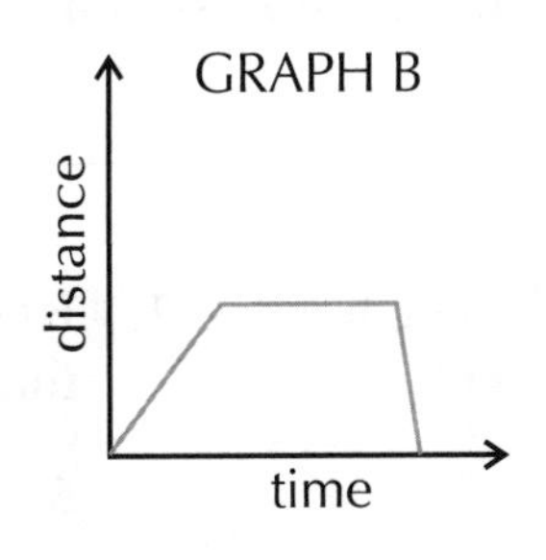

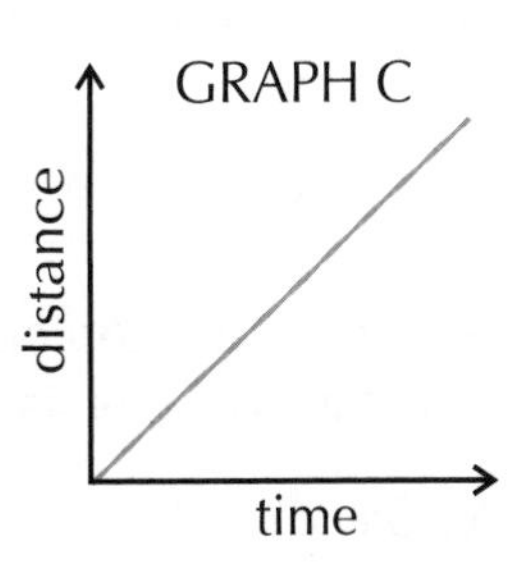

Edward cycles, at a constant speed, from his home to the shop.

....

Edward goes for a walk. He walks at a constant speed, stops to have a picnic, then walks at a constant speed back to his starting point.

....

Edward takes a bus from home to school. It travels at a constant speed, stops to pick up some others, and then continues at a constant speed to school.

....

(2 marks)

6. **Expand and simplify the following expression.**
$(x + 1)(x - 1)(x + 5)$

....

(3 marks)

Score: $\frac{\quad}{10}$

Geometry and Measures: Test 1

Give yourself **10 minutes** to do this test — there are **7 questions** to answer.

Quick-fire Questions

1. A regular octagon has a side length of 8 cm. What is its perimeter?

A 64 cm

B 72 cm

C 80 cm

(1 mark)

2. How many lines of symmetry does this regular shape have?

A 3

B 6

C 12

(1 mark)

3. Find the size of angles x and y in the diagram below, without using a calculator.

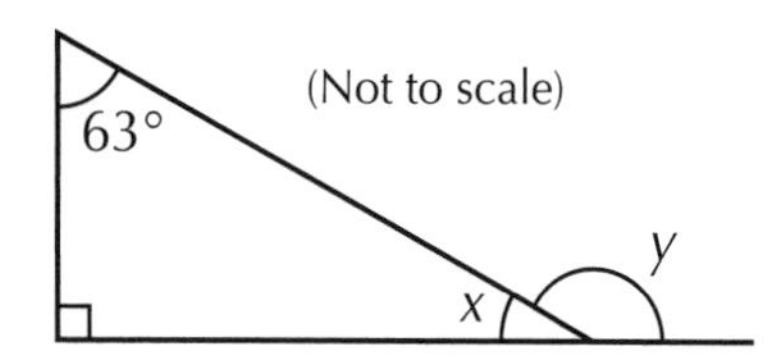

$x =$ .... ° $y =$ .... °

(2 marks)

4. Shape ABCD is shown on the coordinate grid below.

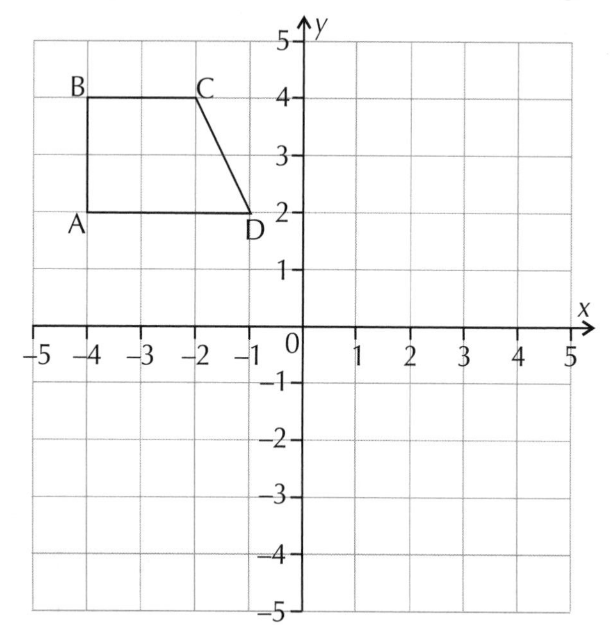

Translate shape ABCD by the vector $\begin{pmatrix} 6 \\ 0 \end{pmatrix}$.

Label the image $A_1B_1C_1D_1$.

(1 mark)

Translate shape $A_1B_1C_1D_1$ by the vector $\begin{pmatrix} -1 \\ -5 \end{pmatrix}$.

Label the image $A_2B_2C_2D_2$.

(1 mark)

5. **Work out the scale factor of enlargement from the smaller circle to the larger circle. Give your answer as a decimal.**

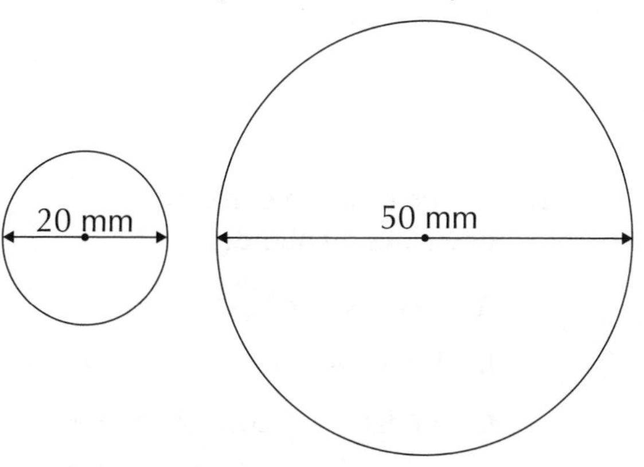

....
(1 mark)

6. **The shape below is a regular decagon.**

Calculate the size of the interior angle marked a.

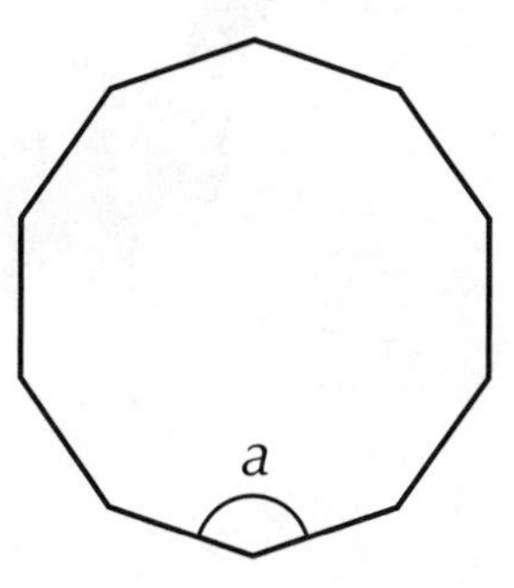

$a =$ .... °
(2 marks)

7. **The diagram below shows two triangles.**

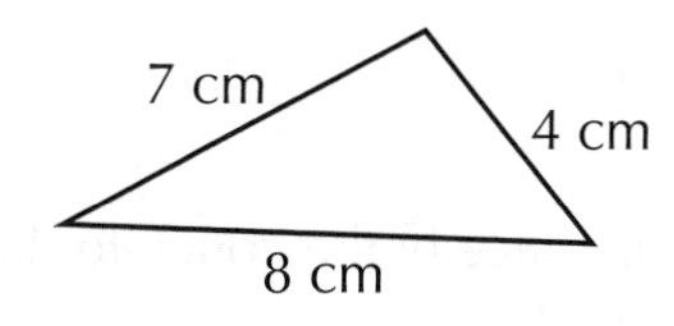

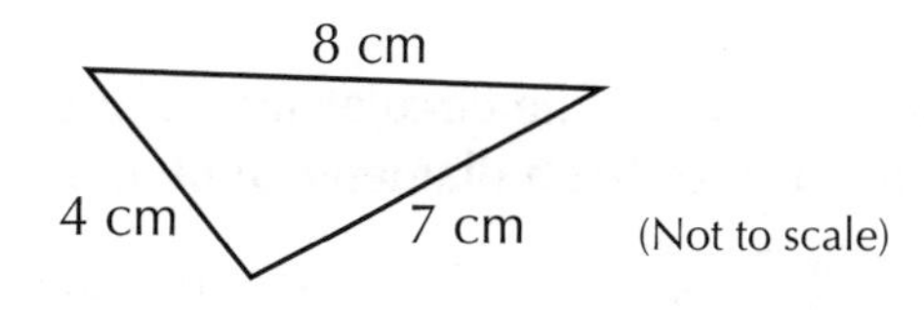

(Not to scale)

Are the two triangles congruent? Explain your answer.

....

....
(1 mark)

Score: ___ / **10**

Geometry and Measures: Test 2

Give yourself **10 minutes** to do this test — there are **6 questions** to answer.

Quick-fire Questions

1. A cylinder has a volume of 90 cm³ and a length of 9 cm. What is the cross-sectional area of the cylinder?

A 810 cm²

B 10 cm²

C 99 cm²

(1 mark)

2. Which of these correctly describes a cuboid?

A 8 edges, 6 faces, 8 vertices

B 12 edges, 6 faces, 8 vertices

C 8 edges, 6 faces, 12 vertices

(1 mark)

3. Find the area of this trapezium without using a calculator.

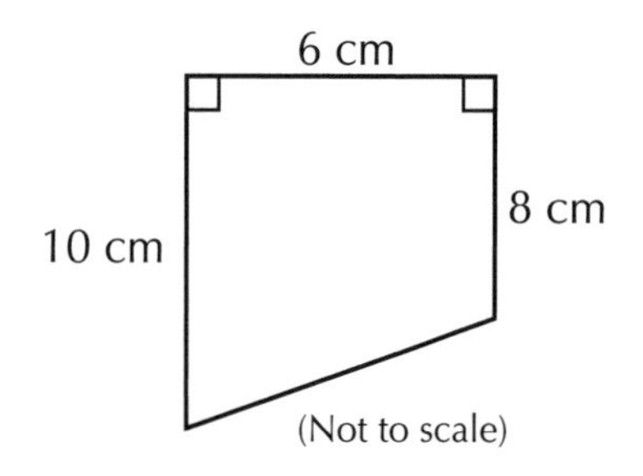

.... cm²
(1 mark)

4. The diagram shows the circular face of a concrete slab. The circular face has a diameter of 60 cm.

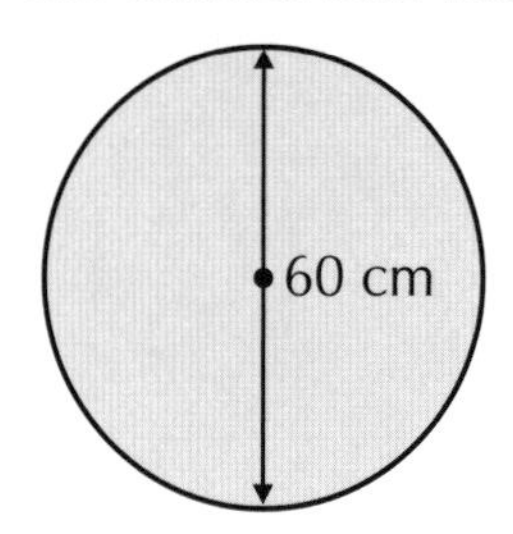

Calculate the area of the circular face of the concrete slab. Give your answer to 3 significant figures.

.... cm²
(2 marks)

5. **The net of a square-based pyramid is made up of four identical isosceles triangles and a square.**

The height of each triangle is 8 cm.
The base of each triangle is half its height.
Calculate the surface area of the square-based pyramid.

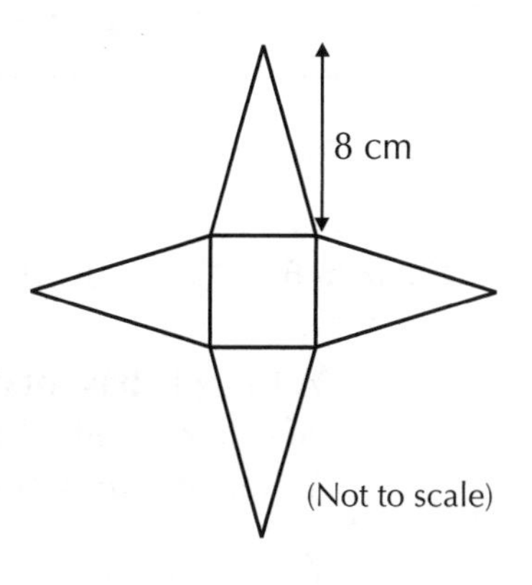

(Not to scale)

.... cm^2
(2 marks)

6. **The rectangle below has a width of 6 cm. Its diagonal is 10 cm long.**

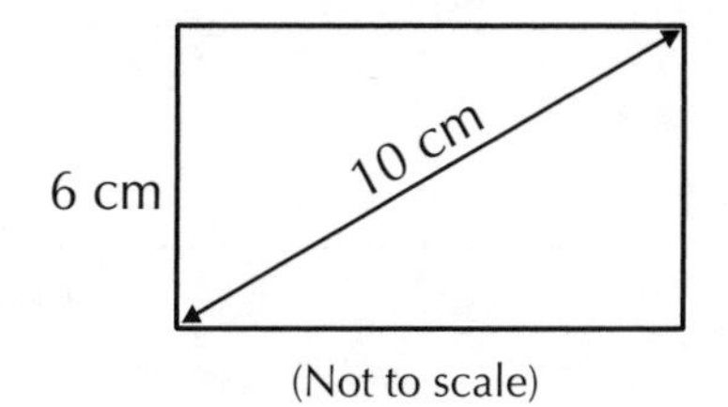

(Not to scale)

Without using a calculator, work out the area of the rectangle.

.... cm^2
(3 marks)

Score: —— / **10**

Bonus Brainteaser

The concrete slab in Q4 is a cylinder with a thickness of 20 cm,
Calculate the exact volume of the slab,
leaving your answer in terms of π.

.... cm^3

Geometry and Measures: Test 3

Give yourself **10 minutes** to do this test — there are **7 questions** to answer.

Quick-fire Questions

1. **A triangle has rotational symmetry of order 1 and 1 line of symmetry. What kind of triangle is it?**

   A Equilateral

   B Isosceles

   C Scalene

   (1 mark)

2. **Which of these stars is similar to star D?**

A 

B 

C

(1 mark)

3. **Find the volume of the cuboid-shaped matchbox shown below.**

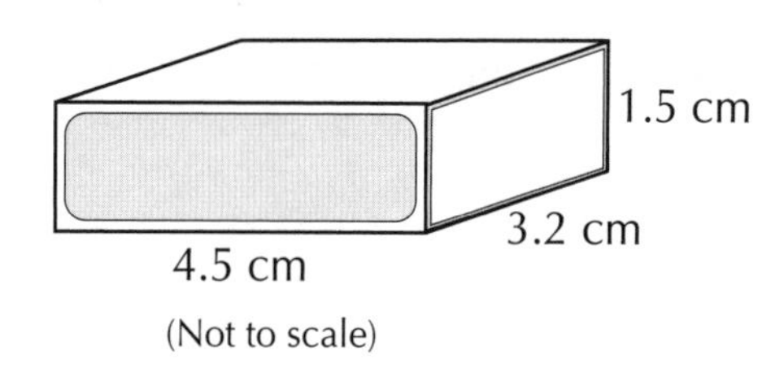

(Not to scale)

.... cm^3

(1 mark)

4. **Trapezium ABCD is shown below. Angle ADC = 73°.**

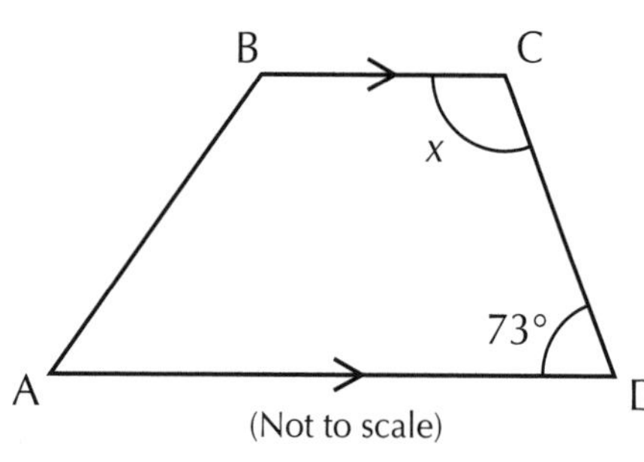

(Not to scale)

Calculate the size of angle x.

x = ...°

(1 mark)

5. **A regular dodecagon has 12 sides. Calculate the size of each of its exterior angles.**

....°

(1 mark)

6. **Shapes A and B are shown on the coordinate grid below.**

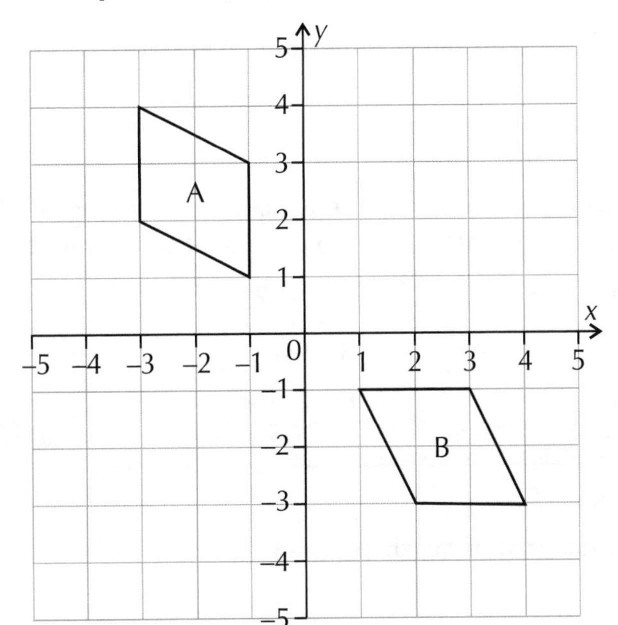

Reflect shape B in the *x*-axis.
Label the reflected shape C.

(1 mark)

Describe the rotation that maps shape A onto shape C.

....

....

....

....

(2 marks)

7. **Triangle RST has sides RS = 4 cm, RT = 5 cm and ST = 6 cm.**

Construct triangle RST in the space above. Side RS has been drawn for you.

(2 marks)

Score: **/ 10**

Geometry and Measures: Test 4

Give yourself **10 minutes** to do this test — there are **6 questions** to answer.

Quick-fire Questions

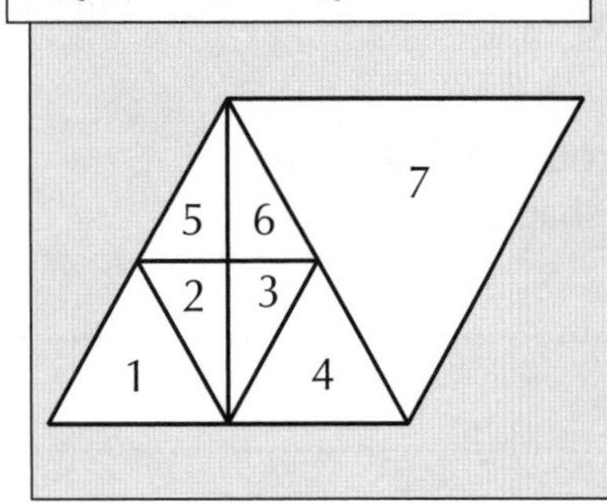

1. Which of these pairs of triangles are congruent?

A 1 and 2

B 1 and 3

C 1 and 4

(1 mark)

2. How many other triangles are congruent to triangle 2?

A One

B Two

C Three

(1 mark)

3. Without using a calculator, work out the total area of the shape below.

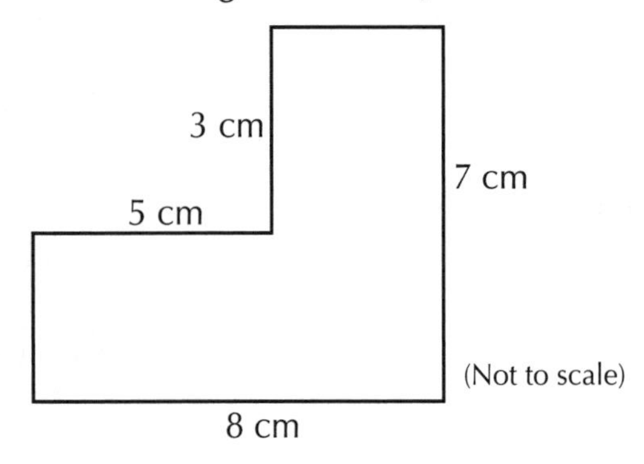

.... cm²

(2 marks)

4. A zookeeper wants to put a railing around the edge of the penguin enclosure. The penguin enclosure is circular and the distance from the centre to the edge is 15 m.

How many metres of railing will the zookeeper need?
Give your answer to 2 decimal places.

.... m

(2 marks)

5. **Shape X and shape Y are shown on this coordinate grid.**

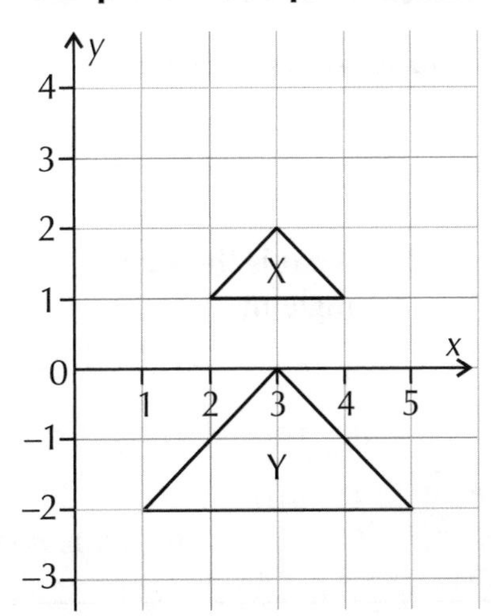

For the enlargement that maps shape X onto shape Y, find:

The scale factor.

....
(1 mark)

The centre of enlargement.

....
(1 mark)

6. **The diagram below shows a cross-section of a roof.**
The roof is 2.5 m tall and at a 34° angle to the horizontal.

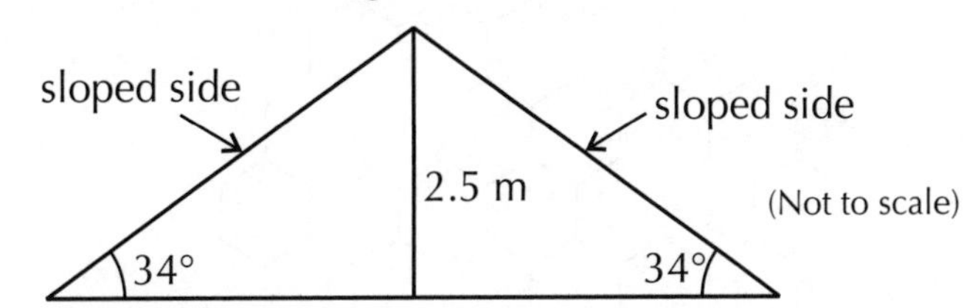

Find the total length of both the sloped sides of the roof.
Give your answer to 2 decimal places.

.... m
(2 marks)

Score: $\frac{\quad}{10}$

Bonus Brainteaser

A zoo recommends penguins have 14 m^2 of space each. What is the maximum number of penguins that could fit in the enclosure in Q4?

....

Geometry and Measures: Test 5

Give yourself **10 minutes** to do this test — there are **7 questions** to answer.

Quick-fire Questions

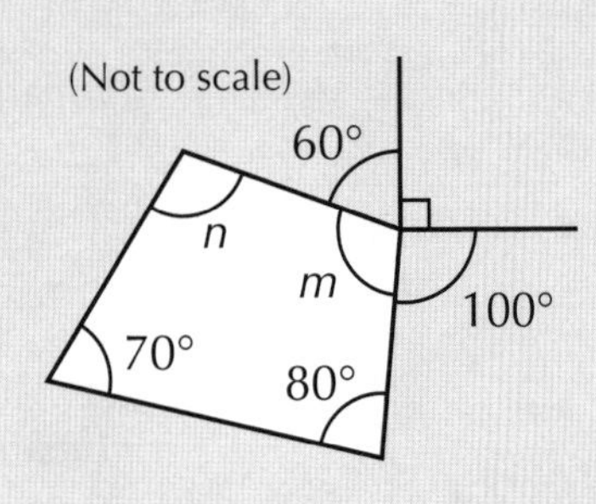

1. **What is the size of angle *m*?**

   A 90°

   B 100°

   C 110°

   (1 mark)

2. **What is the size of angle *n*?**

   A 90°

   B 100°

   C 110°

   (1 mark)

3. **Shade in two more hexagons so that this shape has rotational symmetry of order 3.**

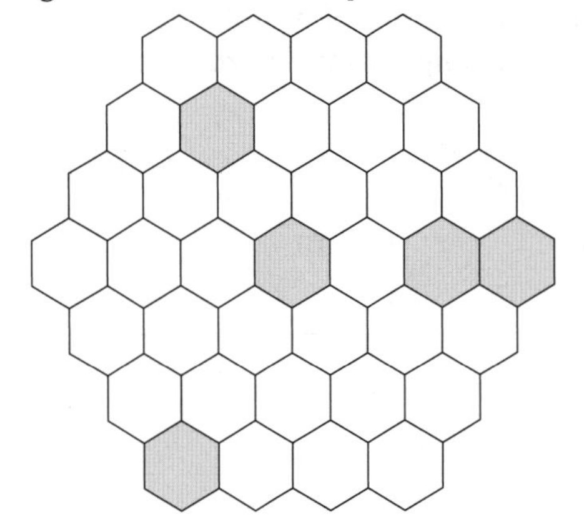

(1 mark)

4. **On the grid below, rotate shape Z 90° anticlockwise about the origin.**

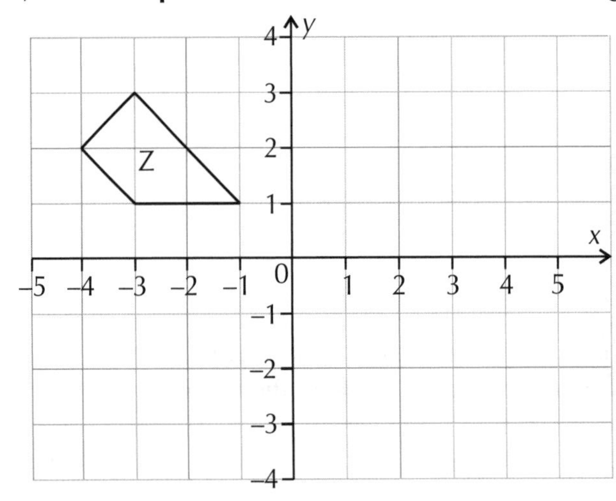

(1 mark)

5. **Amy measures the angles of a pentagon and marks them on the diagram below.**

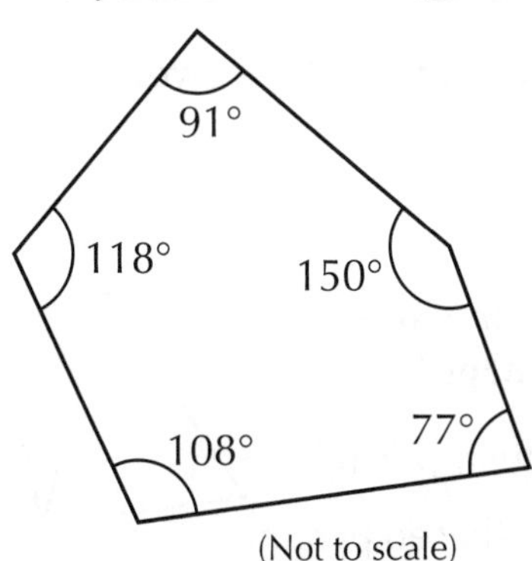

(Not to scale)

Without using a protractor, decide whether Amy's measurements are accurate. Explain your answer.

....

....

....

....

(2 marks)

6. **In the space below, construct the perpendicular bisector of the line AB.**

(2 marks)

7. **Two right-angled triangles are shown below.**

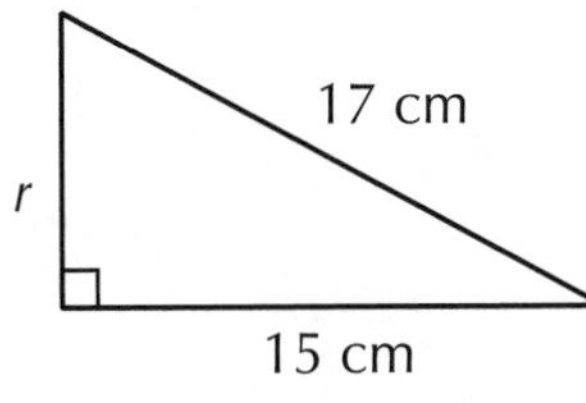

5 cm

13 cm

t

(Not to scale)

Show that side t is longer than side r.

....

....

....

(2 marks)

Score: ___ / **10**

Geometry and Measures: Test 6

Give yourself **10 minutes** to do this test — there are **6 questions** to answer.

Quick-fire Questions

1. **How many faces does a triangular prism have?**

   A 5

   B 6

   C 3

   (1 mark)

2. **What is name of this 3D shape?**

   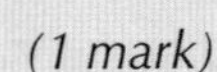

   A triangular prism

   B square-based pyramid

   C tetrahedron

   (1 mark)

3. **The diagram below shows a building and a similar model of the building. The model is 500 times smaller than the building.**

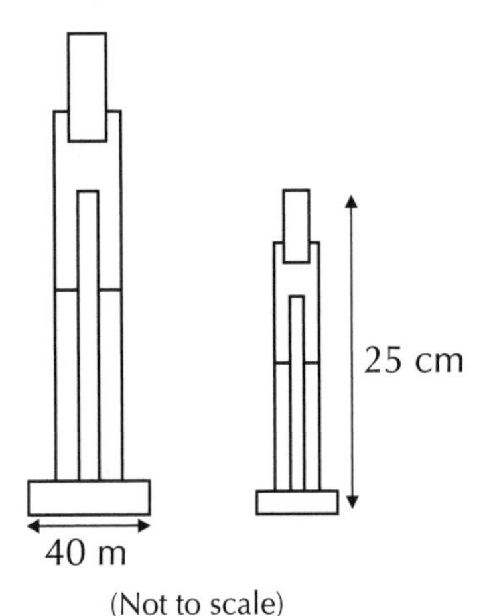

(Not to scale)

The model is 25 cm tall. How tall is the actual building? Give your answer in metres.

.... m
(1 mark)

The base of the building is 40 m wide. How wide is the base of the model? Give your answer in cm.

.... cm
(1 mark)

4. **Find the size of angle ABE in the diagram below. Explain your answer.**

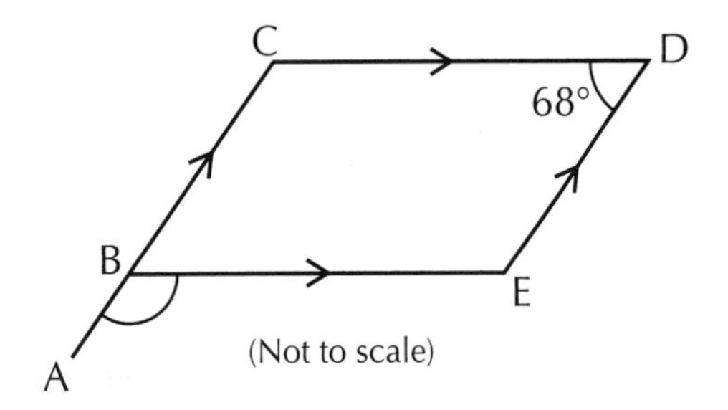

(Not to scale)

....

....

....

....

(1 mark)

5. **In the space below, draw an accurate net of the cuboid on the right. Label the sides.**

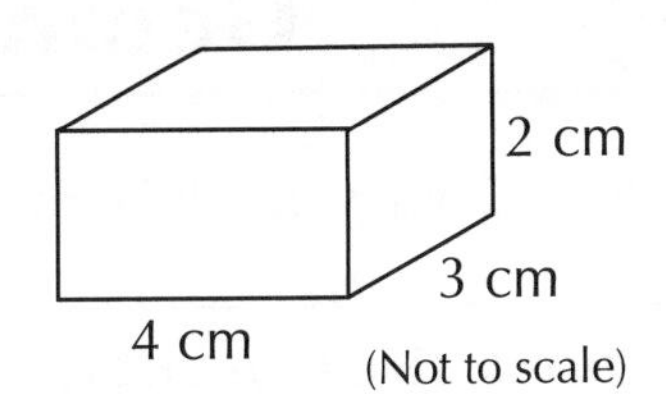

(2 marks)

6. **The diagram below shows a cylinder-shaped tin of paint.**

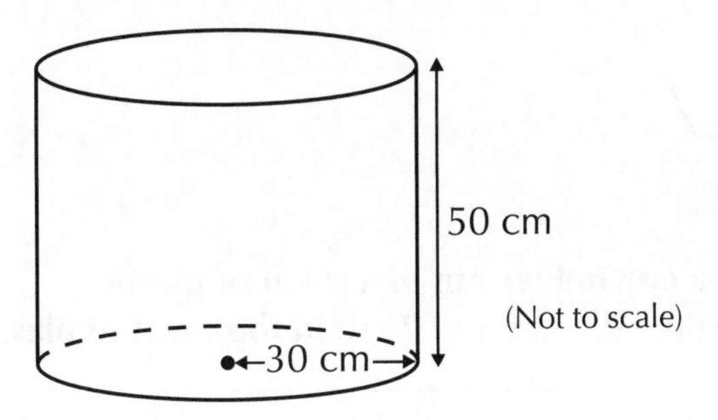

Work out the total surface area of the tin of paint to 3 significant figures.

.... cm^2
(3 marks)

Score: /10

Geometry and Measures: Test 7

Give yourself **10 minutes** to do this test — there are **6 questions** to answer.

Quick-fire Questions

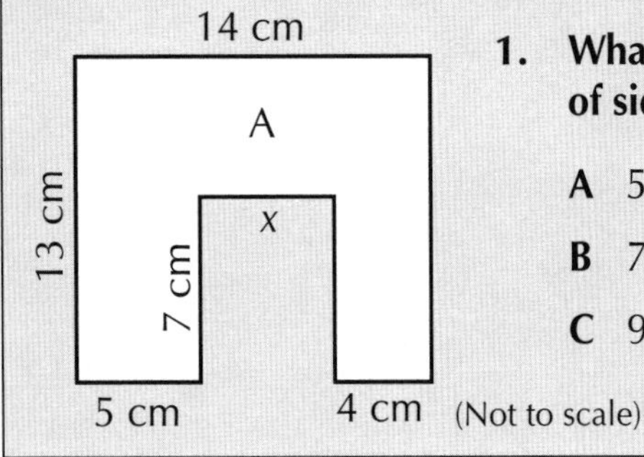

(Not to scale)

1. What is the length of side x?

A 5 cm

B 7 cm

C 9 cm

(1 mark)

2. What is the perimeter of shape A?

A 48 cm

B 61 cm

C 68 cm

(1 mark)

3. Calculate the sum of the interior angles of the shape below.

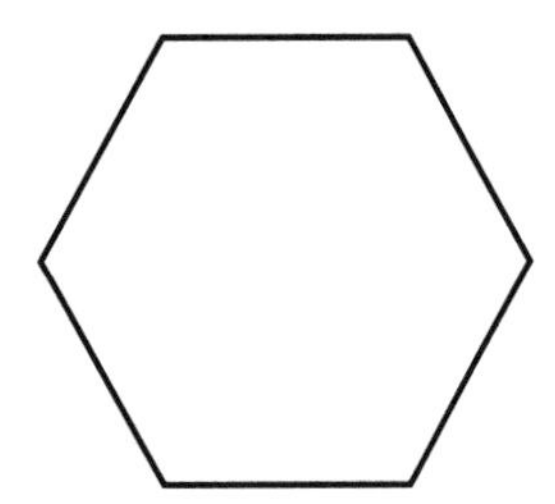

....°

(2 marks)

4. Andreas is making a cup holder out of a sheet of plastic. He drills a circle with a diameter of 7 cm in the sheet of plastic.

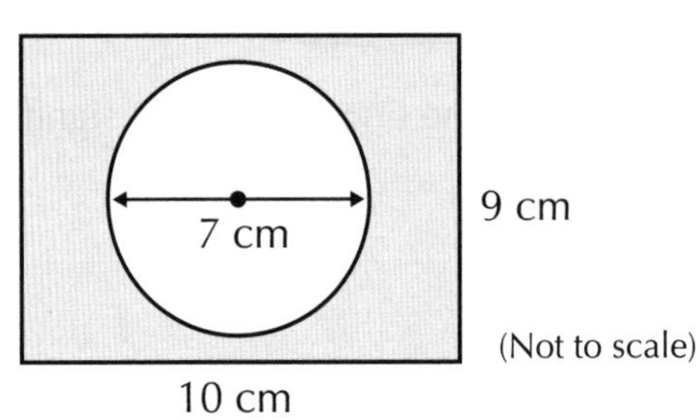

(Not to scale)

What is the remaining area of plastic? Give your answer to 3 significant figures.

.... cm^2

(2 marks)

**5. A cuboid box contains cuboid-shaped dominoes.
The dimensions are shown in the diagram below.**

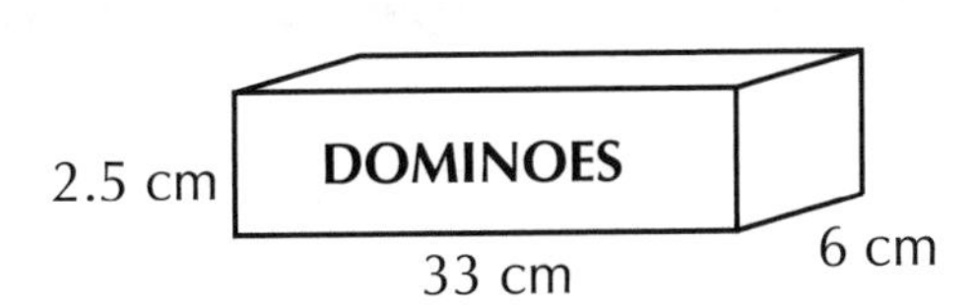

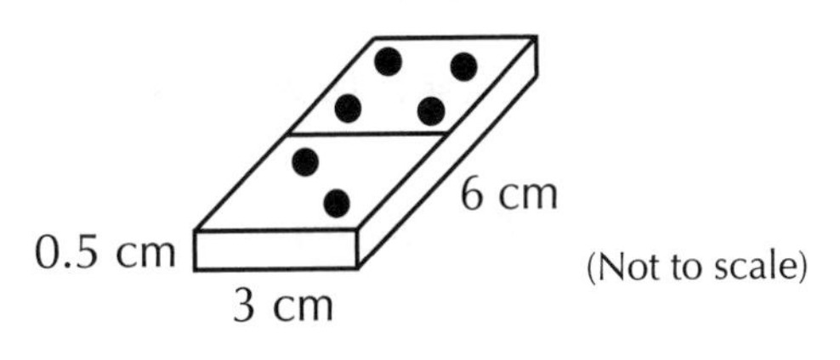

(Not to scale)

What is the maximum number of dominoes that will fit in the box?

....
(2 marks)

**6. A footballer is 20 m away from goal and the ball is on the ground.
He kicks the ball in a straight line and it hits the crossbar which is 2.4 m off the ground.**

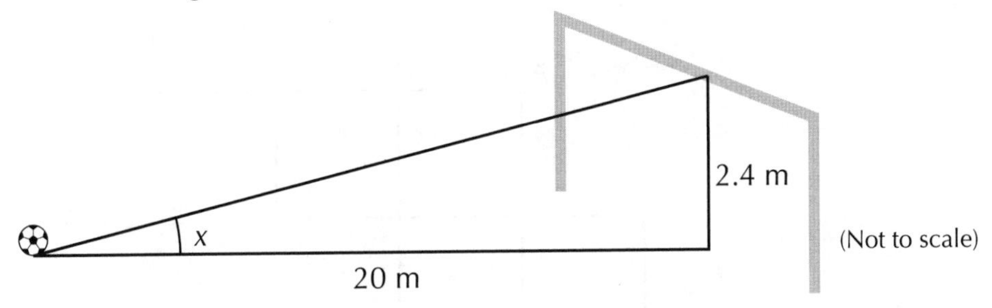

(Not to scale)

Calculate the angle, x, shown in the diagram. Give your answer to 1 decimal place.

x = ... °
(2 marks)

Score: $\frac{\quad}{10}$

Bonus Brainteaser

The footballer in Q6 has another shot that hits the crossbar. This time he is 15 m away from the goal and the ball is 1 m off the ground when he kicks it. Calculate the angle the ball's path makes with the horizontal, to 1 d.p.

.... °

Geometry and Measures: Test 8

Give yourself **10 minutes** to do this test — there are **6 questions** to answer.

Quick-fire Questions 

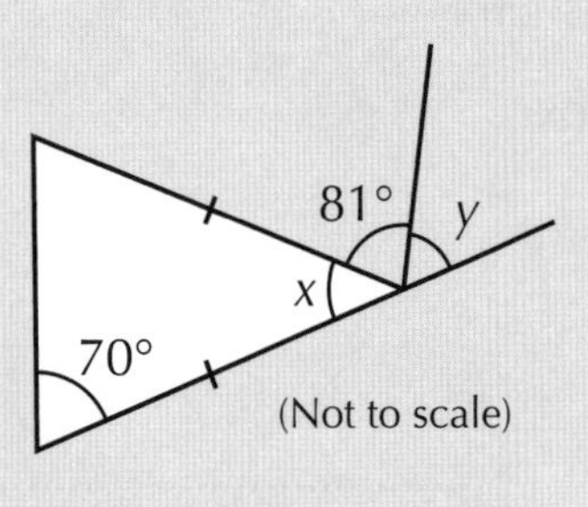

1. What is the size of angle *x*?

A 30°

B 40°

C 50°

(1 mark)

2. What is the size of angle y?

A 59°

B 49°

C 39°

(1 mark)

3. The net of a cube is shown below.

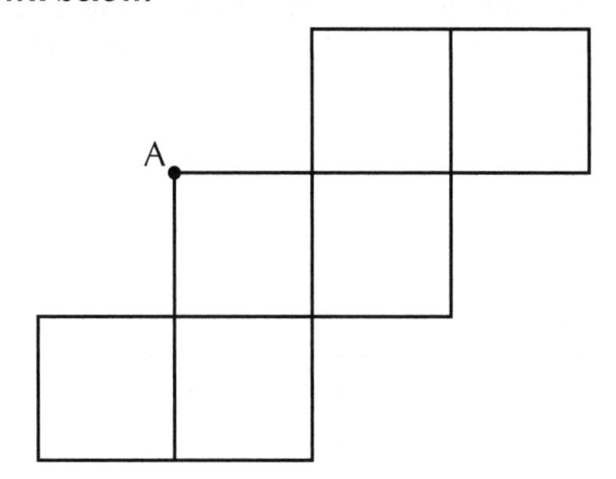

Mark the **two** points on the net that will touch point A when it is folded into a cube.

(1 mark)

4. A copper pipe is in the shape of a cylinder. The radius of the pipe is 1.2 cm.

Calculate the area of the cross-section of the pipe.
Give your answer to 3 significant figures.

.... cm^2

(1 mark)

The pipe is 1 m long. Calculate the volume of the pipe.
Give your answer, in cm^3, to 3 significant figures.

.... cm^3

(1 mark)

5. A 30 m rope is tied to the top of a pole and pulled taut. The rope is pinned to the ground 10 m away from the base of the pole.

What is the height of the pole? Give your answer to 2 d.p.

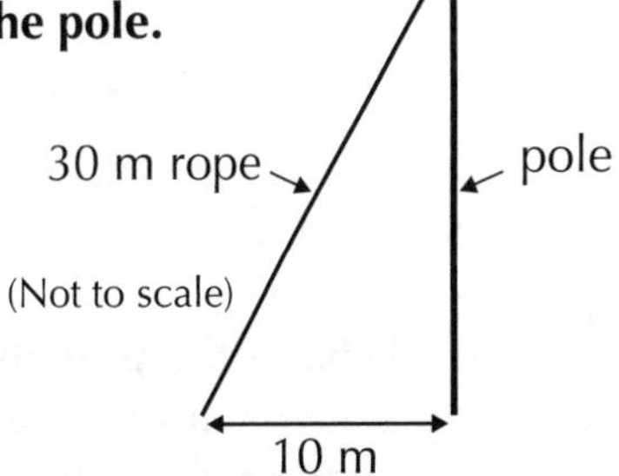

.... m
(2 marks)

6. The dimensions of Stacey's garden are shown in the diagram below.

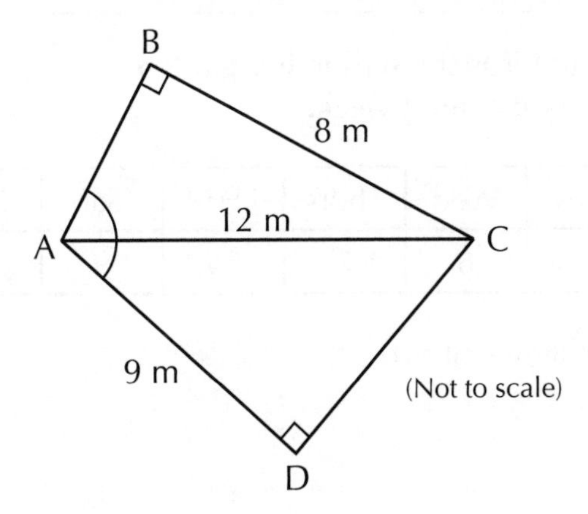

Calculate the size of angle DAB. Give your answer to the nearest whole number.

Angle DAB = ... °
(3 marks)

Score: ___ / **10**

Probability and Statistics: Test 1

Give yourself **10 minutes** to do this test — there are **7 questions** to answer.

Quick-fire Questions

1. What is the probability of picking a 3 from a set of ten cards numbered 1-10?

A $\frac{1}{3}$

B $\frac{1}{10}$

C $\frac{3}{10}$

(1 mark)

2. What is the probability of picking a prime number from a set of twelve cards numbered 1-12?

A $\frac{1}{4}$

B $\frac{1}{2}$

C $\frac{5}{12}$

(1 mark)

3. Meera records the number of birds she sees in her garden between 7 am and 8 am every day for a week.

Mon	Tues	Wed	Thurs	Fri	Sat	Sun
8	12	6	7	15	9	10

Find the range of her results shown above.

....

(1 mark)

4. Cameron has a bag containing 4 red balls, 3 blue balls and 1 green ball. He picks a ball from the bag at random, records the colour and replaces it.

What is the probability of picking a blue ball?

....

(1 mark)

Without using a calculator, work out how many times Cameron would expect to pick a blue ball if he repeated this process 200 times.

....

(1 mark)

5. The graph below shows how far pupils in Class 9A have to travel to school.

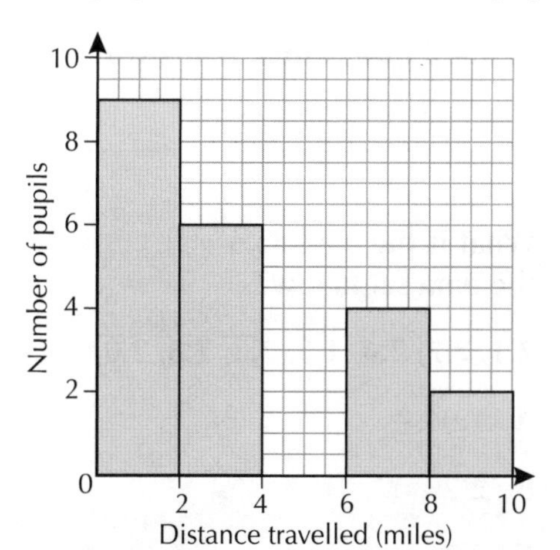

3 pupils travel between 4 and 6 miles to school.
Complete the graph using this information.

(1 mark)

How many pupils travel more than 6 miles to get to school?

....

(1 mark)

6. A fair spinner with 12 equal sections has three sections that are purple.

What is the probability of not spinning purple?
Give your answer as a fraction in its simplest form.

....

(1 mark)

7. Twelve teenagers are timed answering a maths question. Their times (in seconds) are given below.

17	25	21	32	26	18
22	29	26	31	28	18

What is the median time?

.... seconds

(2 marks)

Score: ___ / **10**

Probability and Statistics: Test 2

Give yourself **10 minutes** to do this test — there are **6 questions** to answer.

Quick-fire Questions

1. **What is the mode of the data set below?**

   187, 199, 177, 188, 187, 199, 187

   A 187

   B 199

   C 188

   (1 mark)

2. **What is the median of the data set below?**

   2.1, 2.7, 2.4, 1.9, 2.2, 2.8, 2.0

   A 1.9

   B 2.2

   C 2.3

   (1 mark)

3. **The sample space diagram below shows all the possible outcomes when two identical fair 4-sided spinners are spun.**

	Red (R)	Blue (B)	Green (G)	Yellow (Y)
Red (R)	RR	RB	RG	RY
Blue (B)	BR	BB	BG	BY
Green (G)	GR	GB	GG	GY
Yellow (Y)	YR	YB	YG	YY

What is the probability of spinning the same colour on both spinners? Give your answer as a fraction in its simplest form.

....

(1 mark)

4. **Luke, Evie, Claire and Mohammed are being picked for a team. Claire is always picked first, and a boy is always picked last.**

   List all the possible orders that the children could be chosen in.

....

....

....

....

(1 mark)

5. This scatter graph shows the age and price of some cars.

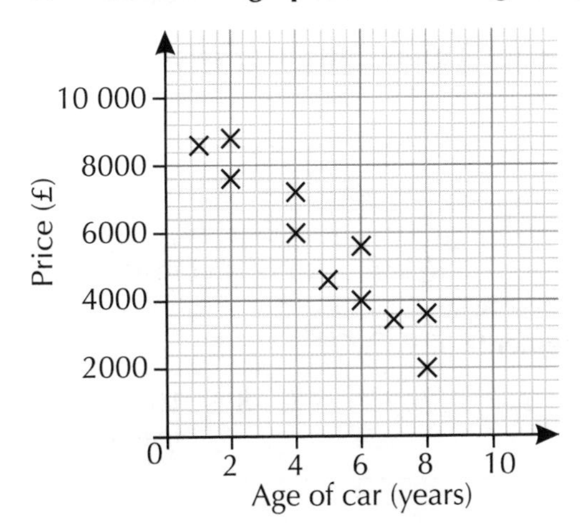

Draw a line of best fit on the graph.

(1 mark)

What type of correlation is shown on the graph?

....

(1 mark)

Use your line of best fit to predict the price of a 9-year-old car.

£ ....

(1 mark)

6. A teacher asked the 30 students in her class if they had been to France or Spain.

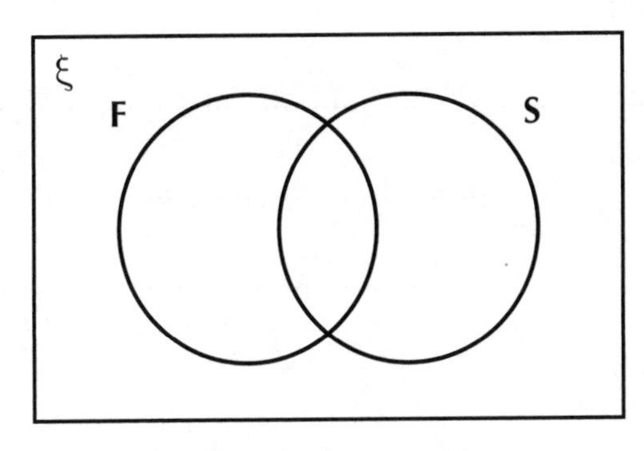

Use the information below to complete the Venn diagram.

- 12 of the class had only been to France,
- 6 had only been to Spain,
- 3 had been to both France and Spain,
- the rest of the class had been to neither France nor Spain.

(2 marks)

The teacher picks one student at random.
What is the probability that they have been to Spain?
Give your answer as a fraction in its simplest form.

....

(1 mark)

Score: $\frac{\quad}{10}$

Bonus Brainteaser

Use your Venn diagram from Q6 to work out the probability that a randomly selected pupil hasn't been to France.
Give your answer as a fraction in its simplest form. ....

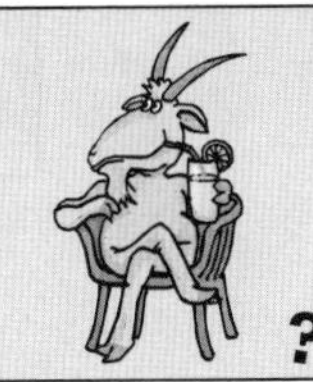

Probability and Statistics: Test 3

Give yourself **10 minutes** to do this test — there are **7 questions** to answer.

Quick-fire Questions

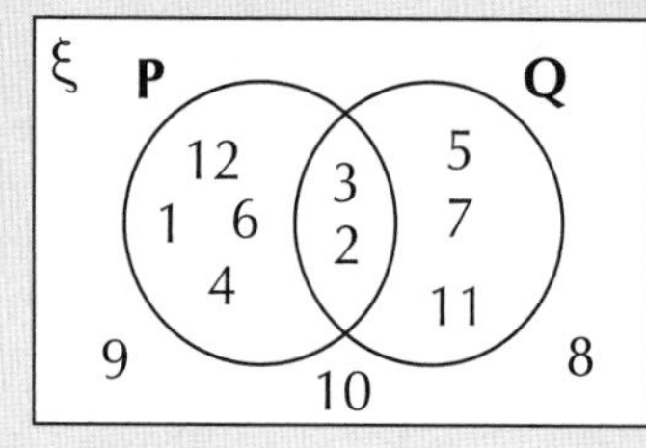

1. What is n(P)?

A 4 **B** 6 **C** 9 *(1 mark)*

2. What are the elements of P ∩ Q?

A 2, 3 **B** 1, 2, 3, 4, 6, 12 **C** 8, 9, 10 *(1 mark)*

3. Sita throws a six-sided dice 150 times. It lands on a six 27 times.

Do you think the dice is fair? Explain your answer.

....

....

....

(1 mark)

4. Jamie asks 60 adults how they travel to work. His results are shown in the table below.

He wants to draw a pie chart to display the results.
Work out the angle he'll need for each sector of the pie chart.

Transport	Walk	Car	Cycle	Train	Other
Frequency	18	31	6	3	2
Angle (°)					

(2 marks)

5. The scatter graph below shows the number of hours 10 cello players spend practising each week, and the mark they got in their cello exam.

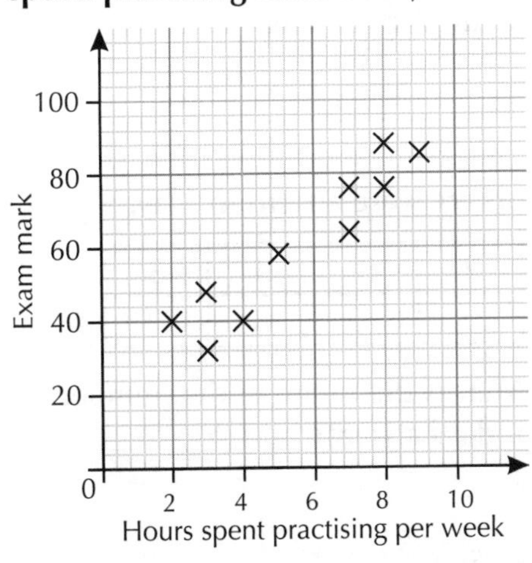

Alfie missed the exam due to illness.
He does 6 hours of practice every week.
By drawing a line of best fit, use the graph to predict the mark he would have got in the exam.

....
(1 mark)

6. Frankie records the time it takes 10 people to complete an orienteering course.

Their times, in minutes, were: 17, 22, 28, 18, 31, 67, 25, 20, 34, 19

Which piece of data do you think could be an outlier?

.... minutes
(1 mark)

7. The grouped frequency table below shows the age in years of 200 people at a rock concert.

Age (years)	15-19	20-24	25-29	30-34	35-39	Total
Frequency	12	28	58	57	45	200

What is the modal age group?

....
(1 mark)

What is the median age group?

....
(2 marks)

Score: ___ / **10**

Probability and Statistics: Test 4

Give yourself **10 minutes** to do this test — there are **6 questions** to answer.

Quick-fire Questions

A manager records the number of days his office workers were absent in May.

Number of days absent in May	0	1	2	3	4	5
Frequency	20	7	9	10	6	0

1. How many people work at the office?

A 15

B 32

C 52

(1 mark)

2. What is the range of the number of days absent?

A 4

B 5

C 3

(1 mark)

3. A jar of sweets contains bonbons, toffees and aniseed balls. The probability of picking a bonbon is $\frac{1}{5}$ and the probability of picking a toffee is $\frac{4}{15}$.

Without using a calculator, work out the probability of picking an aniseed ball. Give your answer as a fraction in its simplest form.

....

(1 mark)

4. A group of people were asked to name their favourite sport. The results were shown in a pie chart.

15 people said their favourite sport was badminton.
The angle of the badminton sector on the pie chart was 72°.

How many people were asked in total?

....

(2 marks)

5. **Carys has a fair 8-sided spinner numbered 1-8. She spins it 100 times and records how many times it lands on each number.**

Fill in the relative frequencies in the table below.

Number	1	2	3	4	5	6	7	8
Frequency	14	7	15	13	16	12	13	10
Relative frequency								

(2 marks)

6. **30 Year 9 students each grew a sunflower. After two weeks, they each recorded the height of their sunflower. The results are shown in the grouped frequency table below.**

Height of sunflower, h (cm)	$0 \le h < 10$	$10 \le h < 20$	$20 \le h < 30$	$30 \le h < 40$	Total
Frequency (f)	4	8	12	6	30
Mid-interval value (x)					—
$f \times x$					

Find an estimate for the mean height of the sunflowers.
Give your answer to 2 decimal places.

.... cm
(3 marks)

Score: ___ / **10**

Answers

Number: Test 1

1. B *(1 mark)*
2. A *(1 mark)*
3. $\begin{array}{r} 1\,4\,1 \\ 12\overline{)1\,6^{4}9^{1}2} \end{array}$ So each bookcase holds 141 books. *(1 mark)*
4. 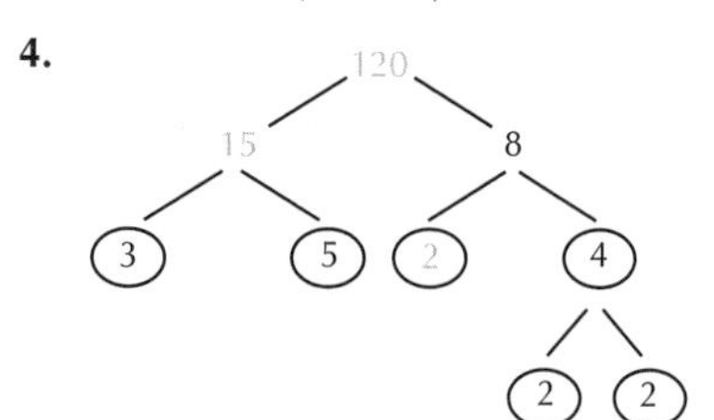

(2 marks available — 1 mark for all the prime factors of 15, 1 mark for all the prime factors of 8).
5. Chris: $\frac{4}{15}$, Teo: $\frac{3}{5} = \frac{9}{15}$, Harry: $\frac{1}{3} = \frac{5}{15}$
Order: Teo, Harry, Chris.
(2 marks available — 1 mark for the fractions over the same denominator, 1 mark for the correct answer.)
6. $2^5 \times 2^6 = 2^{5+6} = 2^{11}$ *(1 mark)*
7. $\sqrt[3]{22\,000} = 28.02039...$ cm
$= 28.02$ cm (2 d.p.)
(2 marks available — 1 mark for using the formula correctly, 1 mark for the correct answer.)

Number: Test 2

1. A *(1 mark)*
2. B *(1 mark)*
3. 17 and 71 have no factors other than 1 and themselves, so they are prime. *(1 mark)*
4. Steady Break: $\frac{11}{42} \times 100 = 26.19...\%$
Maple Rings: $\frac{8}{36} \times 100 = 22.222...\%$
Maple Rings has the lowest percentage of sugar.
(2 marks available — 1 mark for converting scores into percentages, 1 mark for the correct answer.)
5. Multiples of 6: 6, 12, 18, (24), 30, ...
Multiples of 8: 8, 16, (24), 32, 40, ...
Multiples of 12: 12, (24), 36, ...
So the LCM of 6, 8 and 12 is 24.
(2 marks available — 1 mark for using a correct method, 1 mark for the correct answer.)
6. Actual value: 14.39
Rounded value: 14
Error: $14.39 - 14 = 0.39$ s *(1 mark)*
7. $\frac{1 \times p^6}{p^5 \times p^{-2}} = \frac{p^6}{p^3} = p^3$
When $p = 3$, $p^3 = 3^3 = 27$
(2 marks available — 2 marks for the correct answer, otherwise 1 mark for p^3 or 3^3.)

BONUS BRAINTEASER

Actual value: 14.39
Rounded value: 14.4
Error: $14.4 - 14.39 = 0.01$ seconds

Number: Test 3

1. C *(1 mark)*
2. B *(1 mark)*
3. $28 \times 6 = 168$
$17 \times 9 = 153$
$168 + 153 = 321$ *(1 mark)*
4. $\frac{11}{20} \times 600 = 600 \div 20 \times 11$
$= 30 \times 11 = 330$ g *(1 mark)*
5. 17 and –17 *(1 mark)*
7.93 and –7.93 *(1 mark)*
6. $\frac{16\,807}{49} = \frac{7^5}{7^2} = 7^3 = 343$ *(1 mark)*
7. 62 000 *(1 mark)*
$(6.2 \times 10^4) \div (1.4 \times 10^2) = 442.857...$
= 443 to the nearest whole number
(2 marks available — 1 mark for doing the correct division, 1 mark for the correct answer rounded to the nearest whole number.)

Number: Test 4

1. C *(1 mark)*
2. B *(1 mark)*
3. 6.5 *(1 mark)*
0.65 *(1 mark)*
4.

Number of pots	Number of seeds per pot
1	20
2	10
4	5
5	4
10	2
20	1

(1 mark)

5. 3 aubergines: $£0.79 \times 3 = £2.37$
2 parsnips: $£0.47 \times 2 = £0.94$
4 mangoes: $£1.12 \times 4 = £4.48$
$\begin{array}{r} £2.37 \\ £0.94 \\ +\ £4.48 \\ \hline £7.79 \\ {\scriptstyle 1\,1} \end{array}$
(2 marks available — 1 mark for finding the total price for each item, 1 mark for the correct answer.)
6. 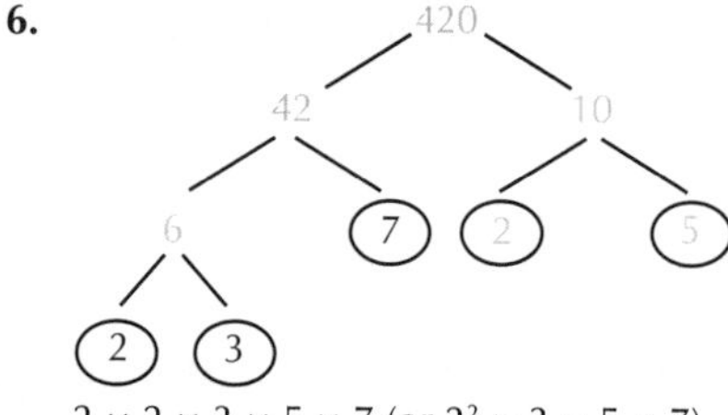

$2 \times 2 \times 3 \times 5 \times 7$ (or $2^2 \times 3 \times 5 \times 7$)
(1 mark)
7. $6\frac{3}{4} + 4\frac{5}{8} = \frac{27}{4} + \frac{37}{8}$
$= \frac{54}{8} + \frac{37}{8}$ *(1 mark)*
$= \frac{91}{8} = 11\frac{3}{8}$ miles *(1 mark)*

BONUS BRAINTEASER

$\frac{3}{5} \times 8 = \frac{3}{5} \times \frac{8}{1} = \frac{24}{5} = 4\frac{4}{5}$ miles

Number: Test 5

1. B *(1 mark)*
2. A *(1 mark)*
3. $\begin{array}{r} 1\,1\,7 \\ 8\overline{)9^{1}4^{6}2} \end{array}$ remainder 6
So he has 6 jewels left over *(1 mark)*
4. Factors of 36: 1, 2, 3, 4, 6, (9), 12, 18, 36
Factors of 63: 1, 3, 7, (9), 21, 63
Factors of 108: 1, 2, 3, 4, 6, (9), 12, 18, 27, 36, 54, 108
So the HCF of 36, 63 and 108 is 9.
(2 marks available — 1 mark for using a correct method, 1 mark for the correct answer).
5. $\frac{8}{15} + \frac{3}{5} = \frac{8}{15} + \frac{9}{15} = \frac{17}{15}$ *(1 mark)*
$\frac{13}{10} - \frac{1}{4} = \frac{26}{20} - \frac{5}{20} = \frac{21}{20}$ *(1 mark)*
6. 9.736×10^5 *(1 mark)*

Answers

7. Small: $834 \times 0.06 = 50.04$ g < 55 g
Med: $906 \times 0.06 = 54.36$ g < 55 g
Large: $963 \times 0.06 = 57.78$ g > 55 g
So it is better value to get 55 g extra of the small and medium cheeses.
(2 marks available — 1 mark for working out 6% of each amount, 1 mark for the correct answer.)

Number: Test 6

1. B *(1 mark)*
2. A *(1 mark)*
3. $\frac{1}{10} = 0.1$ $\quad \frac{1}{2} > 0.2$
$0.7 > \frac{1}{7}$ $\quad 3.5 = \frac{7}{2}$
(2 marks available — 2 marks for all four correct, otherwise 1 mark for any two or three correct.)
4. Multiples of 4:
4, 8, 12, 16, (20), 24 ...
Multiples of 5:
5, 10, 15, (20), ...
So they will both go to Tai Chi together after 20 days. *(1 mark)*
5. $-\frac{2}{3} \times \frac{4}{5} = -\frac{8}{15}$ *(1 mark)*
$\frac{5}{2} \div \frac{3}{8} = \frac{5}{2} \times \frac{8}{3} = \frac{40}{6}$
$= \frac{20}{3} = 6\frac{2}{3}$ *(1 mark)*
6. $17^3 = 4913$ cm^3 *(1 mark)*
7. $\frac{58.7 - 32.4}{2.85 \times 1.9} \approx \frac{60 - 30}{3 \times 2} = \frac{30}{6} = 5$
(2 marks available — 1 mark for rounding all values correctly, 1 mark for the correct answer.)

BONUS BRAINTEASER
$\sqrt[3]{24\,587} = 29.07826...$ m
$= 29.1$ m (3 s.f.)

Number: Test 7

1. A *(1 mark)*
2. C *(1 mark)*
3. 17, 19, 23, 29, 31 *(1 mark)*
4. $\frac{3}{5} \div 4 = \frac{3}{5} \times \frac{1}{4} = \frac{3}{20}$
(2 marks available — 1 mark for using correct reciprocal of 4, 1 mark for correct answer.)
5. 8.97278... = 8.97 (2 d.p.) *(1 mark)*
6. E.g. No, James is not correct. All of the numbers listed are real. *(1 mark)*
7. Upper limit: $213 + (1 \div 2) = 213.5$ *(1 mark)*
Lower limit: $213 - (1 \div 2) = 212.5$ *(1 mark)*
8. From the table, $64 = 4^3$ and $1024 = 4^5$, so $64 \times 1024 = 4^3 \times 4^5 = 4^8 = 65\,536$ *(1 mark)*

Number: Test 8

1. C *(1 mark)*
2. B *(1 mark)*
3. $(-14) + (-27) - (-43) = -14 - 27 + 43 = -41 + 43 = 2$ *(1 mark)*
4. $$\begin{array}{r} \text{£}5\overset{4}{\cancel{0}}.\overset{9}{\cancel{0}}\overset{9}{0} \\ -\text{£}34.64 \\ \hline \text{£}15.36 \end{array}$$ *(1 mark)*
5. 0.22, $\frac{17}{100} = 0.17$, $19\% = 0.19$, $\frac{4}{25} = 0.16$, 0.18
Order: 0.16, 0.17, 0.18, 0.19, 0.22
$= \frac{4}{25}, \frac{17}{100}$, 0.18, 19%, 0.22
(2 marks available — 1 mark for changing all the numbers into the same form, 1 mark for ordering them correctly.)
6. Upper $= 4650 + (10 \div 2) = 4655$
Lower $= 4650 - (10 \div 2) = 4645$
$4645 \le h < 4655$
(or $4645 \le h \le 4654$)
(2 marks available — 1 mark for correct upper and lower limit, 1 mark for the correct inequality.)
7. 0.02 mph $= 2 \times 10^{-3}$ mph *(1 mark)*
$\frac{1}{500} \times \frac{1}{10} = (2 \times 10^{-3}) \times 10^{-1} = 2 \times 10^{-4}$ *(1 mark)*

Ratio, Proportion and Rates of Change: Test 1

1. B *(1 mark)*
2. C *(1 mark)*
3. 1 : 5 *(1 mark)*
4. There are half as many farmers ($8 \div 4 = 2$) so it will take twice as long. $1 \times 2 = 2$ days *(1 mark)*
5. 1 shirt: $15 \div 20 = 0.75$ mins *(1 mark)*
32 shirts: $0.75 \times 32 = 24$ minutes *(1 mark)*
6. 20% increase = 1.2
£480 × 1.2 = £576 *(1 mark)*
7. $7.2 \times 150 = 1080$ cm *(1 mark)*
$1080 \div 100 = 10.8$ m *(1 mark)*
8. Density $= 8610 \div 0.82 = 10500$ kg/m^3 *(1 mark)*

Ratio, Proportion and Rates of Change: Test 2

1. A *(1 mark)*
2. B *(1 mark)*
3. 1 stone 11 lbs $= (1 \times 14) + 11 = 25$ lbs *(1 mark)*
$25 \times 16 = 400$ ounces *(1 mark)*
4. Sm: £1.20 ÷ 10 = £0.12 per pickle
Med: £3.60 ÷ 40 = £0.09 per pickle
Lg: £11.00 ÷ 100 = £0.11 per pickle
So the medium jar is the best value.
(3 marks available — 1 mark for finding the price per pickle for 2 jars, 1 mark for finding it for the third jar, 1 mark for the correct answer.)
5. 3.5% = 0.035
£200 × 0.035 = £7
£7 × 4 = £28 *(1 mark)*
6. Distance $= 6 \times 3.5 = 21$ km *(1 mark)*
$5 \times 1.6 = 8$ km
Total distance $= 21 + 8 = 29$ km *(1 mark)*

BONUS BRAINTEASER
Mass $= 819 \div 1000 = 0.819$ kg
Density $= 0.819 \div 780 = 0.00105$ kg/cm^3

Ratio, Proportion and Rates of Change: Test 3

1. B *(1 mark)*
2. C *(1 mark)*

3. $8 \times 2 = 16$ km *(1 mark)*

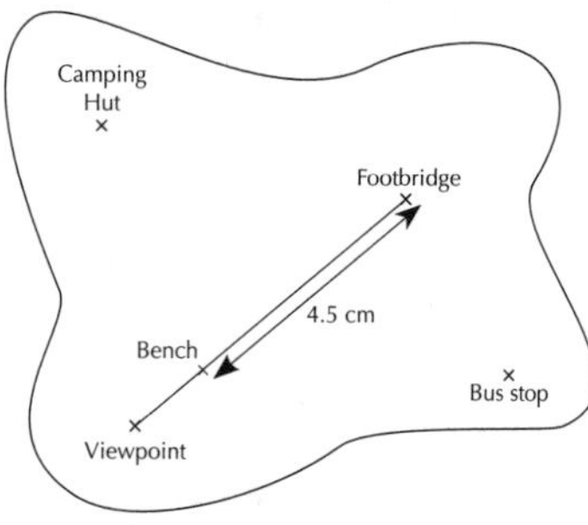

(1 mark)

4. $27 \div 6 = 4.5$ minutes *(1 mark)*

5. Time = 45 minutes = 0.75 hours *(1 mark)*
   Speed = $18 \div 0.75 = 24$ km/h *(1 mark)*

6. There are 11 parts
   1 part = $55 \div 11 = 5$ animals
   5 parts = $5 \times 5 = 25$, so there are 25 pygmy goats. *(1 mark)*
   15 pygmy goats = 5 parts
   1 part = $15 \div 5 = 3$ animals.
   $11 - 5 = 6$ parts, so there are
   $3 \times 6 = 18$ miniature pigs
   (2 marks available — 1 mark for finding the number of animals in one part and 1 mark for finding the number of miniature pigs.)

Ratio, Proportion and Rates of Change: Test 4

1. C *(1 mark)*

2. A *(1 mark)*

3. Profit = £187 500 – £150 000
   = £37 500 *(1 mark)*
   (£37 500 ÷ £150 000) × 100
   = 25% profit *(1 mark)*

4. E.g.

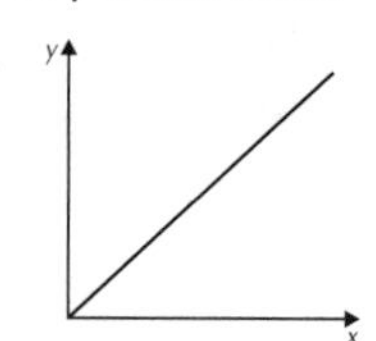

(1 mark for a straight line going through the origin.)

5. 1 person: $240 \div 10 = 24$ g *(1 mark)*
   44 people: $24 \times 44 = 1056$ g *(1 mark)*

6. $150 = \frac{k}{4}$
   $150 \times 4 = k$, $600 = k$ *(1 mark)*
   So $L = \frac{600}{d}$ *(1 mark)*

7. 60% = £39
   10% = £39 ÷ 6 = £6.50.
   100% = £6.50 × 10 = £65 *(1 mark)*

Algebra: Test 1

1. C *(1 mark)*

2. A *(1 mark)*

3. $16n = 32n \div 2$
   So, $16n = 288 \div 2$
   $= 144$ *(1 mark)*

4.

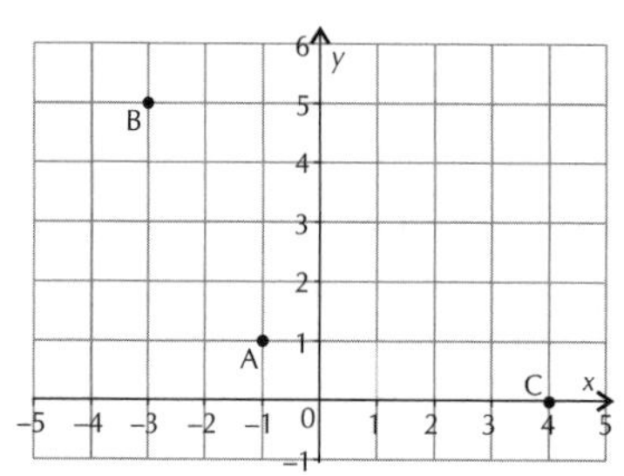

(1 mark)

x-coordinate = $\frac{-1+(-3)}{2} = -2$
y-coordinate = $\frac{1+5}{2} = 3$
So midpoint of AB = (–2, 3) *(1 mark)*

5. E.g. $2N + 5 = 15$ *(1 mark)*

6. Put $x = 3$ into each equation:
   $2x + y = 7$: $2 \times 3 + y = 7$
   $6 + y = 7$, so $y = 1$ ✔
   $3x + 8 = y$: $3 \times 3 + 8 = y$
   $9 + 8 = y$, so $y = 17$ ✘
   $x + 2y = 7$: $3 + 2y = 7$
   $2y = 4$, so $y = 2$ ✘
   $3x - y = 8$: $3 \times 3 - y = 8$
   $9 - y = 8$, so $y = 1$ ✔
   $2x + y = 7$ *(1 mark)* and
   $3x - y = 8$ *(1 mark)*

7. $C = 5 + 2d$
   $C - 5 = 2d$ *(1 mark)*
   $d = \frac{C-5}{2}$ *(1 mark)*

BONUS BRAINTEASER
2 weeks: $2 \times 7 = 14$ days
$C = 5 + 2 \times 14 = 5 + 28 = £33$

Algebra: Test 2

1. A *(1 mark)*

2. C *(1 mark)*

3. 17, 27, 37, 47, 57 *(1 mark)*

4. £8 *(1 mark)*

5. $(x + 5)(x - 4) = x^2 - 4x + 5x - 20$
   $= x^2 + x - 20$ *(1 mark)*

6. $\frac{x}{8} + 2 = -8$
   $\frac{x}{8} = -10$ *(1 mark)*
   so $x = -80$ *(1 mark)*

7. $12ab^2 - 9ab^3 + 24ab$
   $= 3(4ab^2 - 3ab^3 + 8ab)$
   $= 3a(4b^2 - 3b^3 + 8b)$
   $= 3ab(4b - 3b^2 + 8)$
   (3 marks available — 3 marks for correct answer, otherwise 1 mark for correctly taking 1 factor outside the brackets or 2 marks for correctly taking 2 factors outside the brackets.)

Algebra: Test 3

1. C *(1 mark)*

2. C *(1 mark)*

3. Substitute into the formula:
   $L = 60 \times (-0.1) + \frac{1}{2} \times 8^2$
   $L = -6 + 32$
   $L = 26$ *(1 mark)*

4. x-coordinate = $\frac{-3+3}{2} = 0$
   y-coordinate = $\frac{5+(-3)}{2} = 1$
   So midpoint of XY = (0, 1) *(1 mark)*
   x-coordinate = $\frac{-3+3}{2} = 0$
   y-coordinate = $\frac{-1+(-3)}{2} = -2$
   So midpoint of WY = (0, –2) *(1 mark)*

5. Width = $\frac{\text{area}}{\text{length}}$
   Width = $\frac{8p - 5pq}{p}$ *(1 mark)*
   $= 8 - 5q$ *(1 mark)*

6.

x	0	1	2	3
y	–2	1	4	7

(1 mark)

Answers

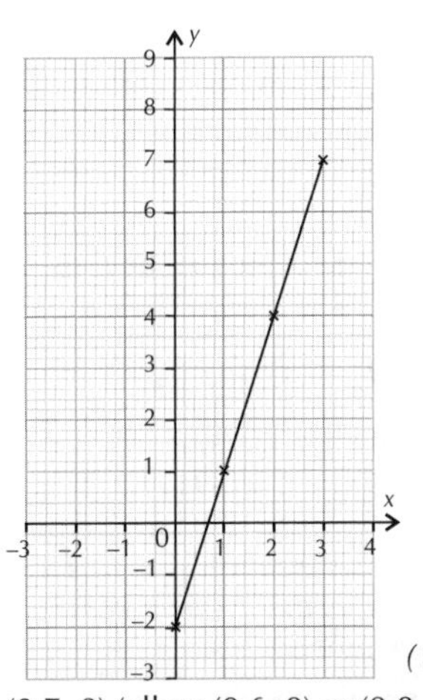

(1 mark)

(0.7, 0) (allow (0.6, 0) or (0.8, 0)) *(1 mark)*

BONUS BRAINTEASER

$x = 1.2$ (allow 1.1 to 1.3)
$y = 1.6$ (allow 1.5 to 1.7)

Algebra: Test 4:

1. A *(1 mark)*
2. A *(1 mark)*
3. $46 < w < 54$ *(1 mark)*
4. $5(3x - 9) = 5x + 15$
   $15x - 45 = 5x + 15$
   $15x = 5x + 60$ *(1 mark)*
   $10x = 60$ so $x = 6$ *(1 mark)*
5. $x = 2$, $y = 3$ *(1 mark)*
6. $4h + 0.5w$ *(1 mark)*
7. $\frac{x-9}{8} = \frac{x-6}{2}$
   $x - 9 = \frac{8(x-6)}{2}$
   $x - 9 = 4(x - 6)$ *(1 mark)*
   $x - 9 = 4x - 24$
   $15 = 3x$ *(1 mark)*
   $x = 5$ *(1 mark)*

Algebra: Test 5

1. B *(1 mark)*
2. C *(1 mark)*
3. Gradient of DE: $\frac{3-1}{2-1} = \frac{2}{1} = 2$ *(1 mark)*
   Gradient of DF: $\frac{5-1}{-3-1} = \frac{4}{-4} = -1$ *(1 mark)*
4. $(2t - 2)^2$ *(1 mark)*
5. 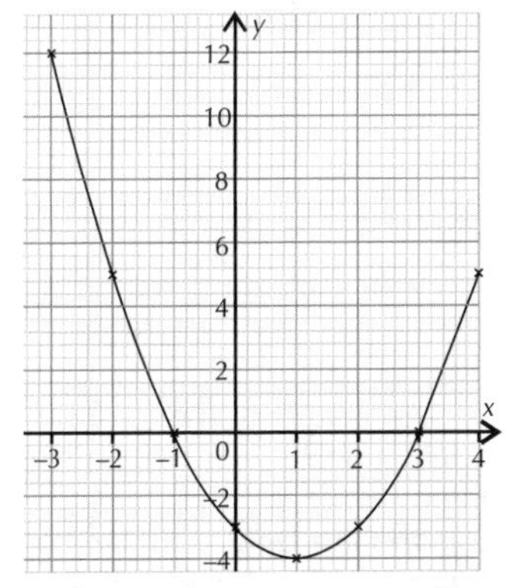

   (1 mark)

   $x = -0.4$ (allow -0.3 to -0.5) *(1 mark)* and $x = 2.4$ (allow 2.3 to 2.5) *(1 mark)*
6. $s = \frac{1}{2}(u + v)t$
   $2s = (u + v)t$ *(1 mark)*
   $\frac{2s}{u+v} = t$ *(1 mark)*

BONUS BRAINTEASER

$\frac{2s}{t} = u + v$, so $v = \frac{2s}{t} - u$

Algebra: Test 6

1. C *(1 mark)*
2. A *(1 mark)*
3. $4 - 6h = -14$
   $4 + 14 = 6h$
   $18 = 6h$ so $h = 3$ *(1 mark)*
4. $\frac{9-3}{5p-3p} = \frac{6}{2p}$ *(1 mark)*
   $\frac{6}{2p} = 3$
   $6 = 6p$
   $p = 1$ *(1 mark)*
5.  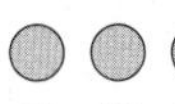 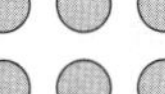  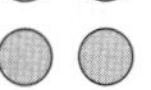 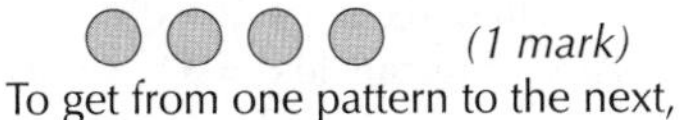

   (1 mark)

   To get from one pattern to the next, you add 3 dots — so the nth term contains $3n$. The 1st pattern has 5 dots in, so to get from $3 \times 1 = 3$ to 5, you add 2. So the nth term is $3n + 2$.
   (2 marks available — 2 marks for correct answer, otherwise 1 mark for $3n$.)
6. $y = 1$ *(1 mark)* $x = -2$ *(1 mark)*

Algebra: Test 7

1. A *(1 mark)*
2. C *(1 mark)*
3. 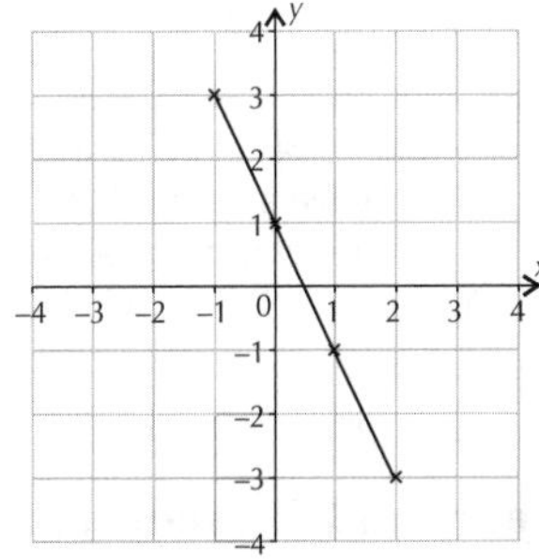

   (1 mark)
   a = −2, b = 1 *(1 mark)*
4. 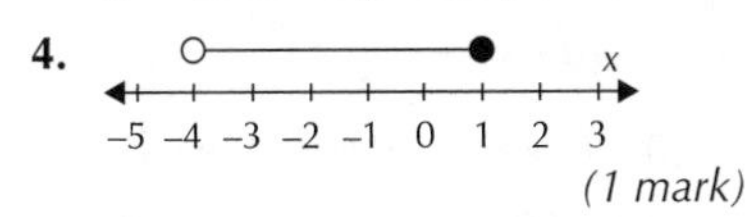

   (1 mark)
5. C, B, A *(2 marks available — 2 marks for all 3 correct answers, otherwise 1 mark for any 1 correct answer.)*
6. $(x + 1)(x - 1)(x + 5)$
   $= (x^2 - 1)(x + 5) = x^3 + 5x^2 - x - 5$
   (3 marks available — 3 marks for fully correct answer, otherwise 1 mark for multiplying out any two brackets correctly and 1 mark for three terms correct in final answer.)

Geometry and Measures: Test 1

1. A *(1 mark)*
2. B *(1 mark)*
3. $x = 180° - 90° - 63° = 27°$ *(1 mark)*
   $y = 180° - 27° = 153°$ *(1 mark)*
4. 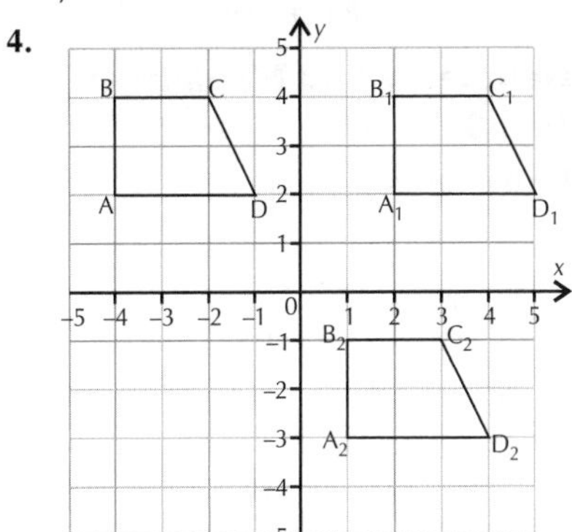

(1 mark for shape $A_1B_1C_1D_1$ drawn in the correct position, 1 mark for shape $A_2B_2C_2D_2$ drawn in the correct position.)

5. $50 \div 20 = 2.5$ *(1 mark)*
6. Exterior angle = $360° \div 10 = 36°$
   Interior angle = $180° - 36° = 144°$
   (2 marks available — 1 mark for using a correct method, 1 mark for the correct answer.)
7. Yes, all 3 sides are the same in both triangles. *(1 mark)*

Geometry and Measures: Test 2

1. B *(1 mark)*
2. B *(1 mark)*
3. $\frac{1}{2}(10 + 8) \times 6 = 54$ cm² *(1 mark)*
4. Radius = $60 \div 2 = 30$ cm *(1 mark)*
   Area = $\pi \times 30^2$
   = 2827.4333... cm²
   = 2830 cm² (3 s.f.) *(1 mark)*
5. Base of triangle = $8 \div 2 = 4$ cm
   Area of triangle = $\frac{1}{2} \times 4 \times 8$
   = 16 cm² *(1 mark)*
   Area of square = $4 \times 4 = 16$ cm²
   Total surface area = $(4 \times 16) + 16$
   = 80 cm² *(1 mark)*
6. Use Pythagoras' Theorem to find the length of the rectangle:
   $10^2 - 6^2 = 64$ *(1 mark)*
   $\sqrt{64} = 8$ cm *(1 mark)*
   Area of rectangle = 6×8
   = 48 cm² *(1 mark)*

BONUS BRAINTEASER
Volume = $\pi \times 30^2 \times 20$
= $18\,000\pi$ cm³

Geometry and Measures: Test 3

1. B *(1 mark)*
2. A *(1 mark)*
3. Volume = $4.5 \times 3.2 \times 1.5$
   = 21.6 cm³ *(1 mark)*
4. BCD and ADC are allied angles:
   $x = 180° - 73° = 107°$ *(1 mark)*
5. $360° \div 12 = 30°$ *(1 mark)*
6. 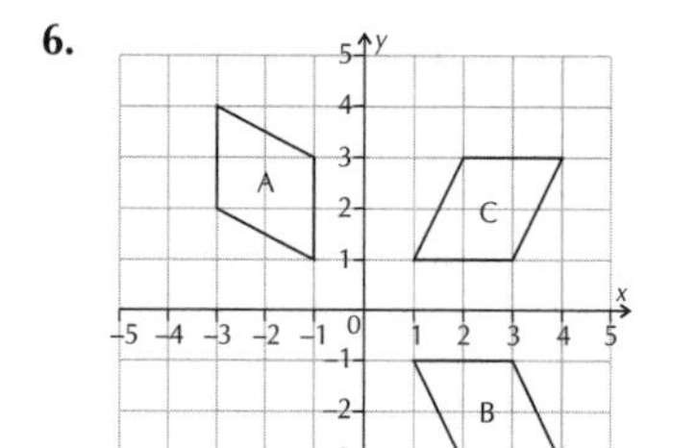

   (1 mark)
   Rotation by 90° clockwise about the origin.
   (2 marks available — 1 mark for '90° clockwise', 1 mark for 'about the origin' or 'about the point (0, 0)'.)
7. 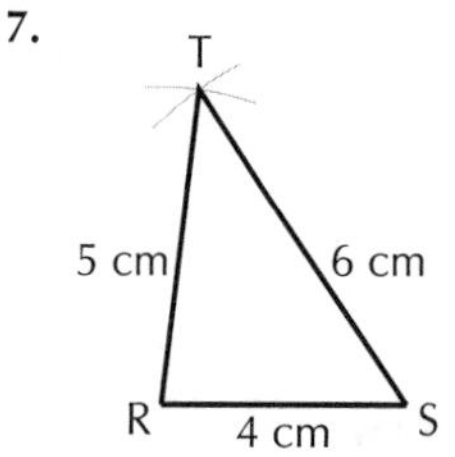

   (2 marks available — 1 mark for the correct construction marks, 1 mark for a correctly drawn shape.)

Geometry and Measures: Test 4

1. C *(1 mark)*
2. C *(1 mark)*
3. 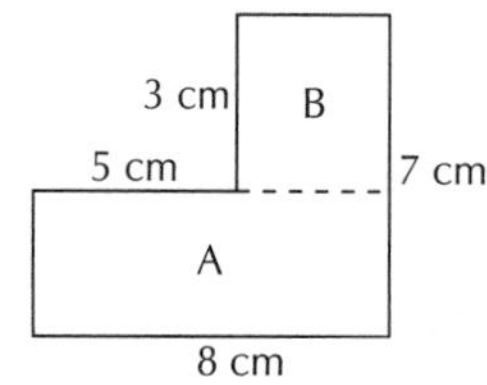

   Width of rectangle A = $7 - 3 = 4$ cm
   Area of rectangle A = $8 \times 4 = 32$ cm²
   Length of rectangle B = $8 - 5 = 3$ cm
   Area of rectangle B = $3 \times 3 = 9$ cm²
   Total area = $32 + 9 = 41$ cm²
   (2 marks available — 1 mark for a correct method, 1 mark for the correct answer.)
4. Diameter = $15 \times 2 = 30$ m *(1 mark)*
   Circumference = $\pi \times 30$
   = 94.2477...
   = 94.25 m (2 d.p.) *(1 mark)*
5. Scale factor = $4 \div 2 = 2$ *(1 mark)*
   Drawing lines through corresponding vertices of shapes X and Y gives the centre of enlargement as (3, 4).
   (1 mark)
6. Let one side of the roof be r, then:
   $\sin 34° = \frac{2.5}{r}$
   $r = \frac{2.5}{\sin 34°} = 4.4707...$ m
   Total length of the roof
   = $4.4707... \times 2 = 8.9414...$
   = 8.94 m (2 d.p.)
   (2 marks available — 1 mark for a correct method, 1 mark for the correct answer.)

BONUS BRAINTEASER
Area of penguin enclosure
= $\pi \times 15^2 = 706.8583...$ m²
$706.8583... \div 14 = 50.4898...$
So you can fit a maximum of 50 penguins in the enclosure.

Geometry and Measures: Test 5

1. C *(1 mark)*
2. B *(1 mark)*
3. 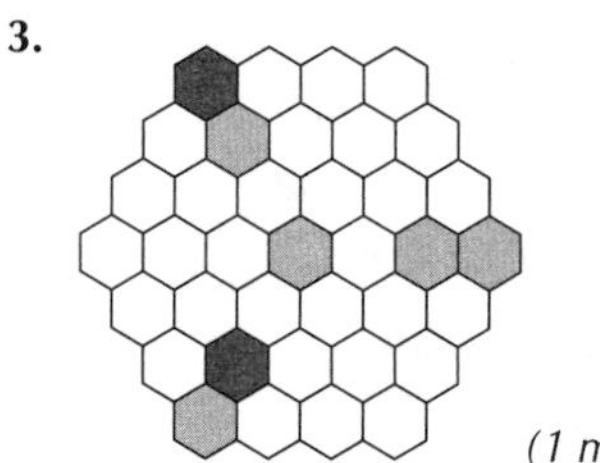
   (1 mark)
4. 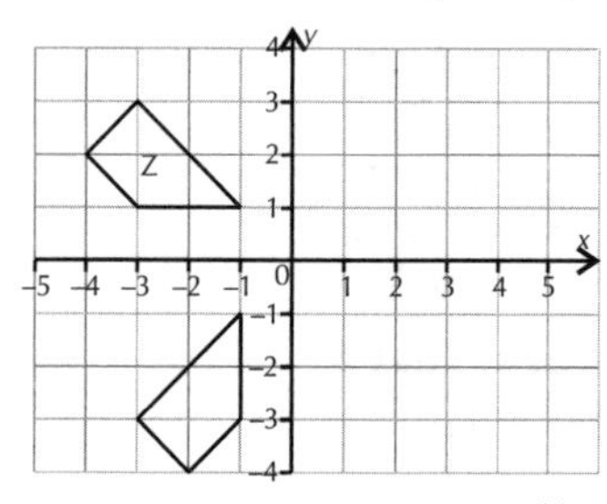

   (1 mark)
5. Interior angles of a pentagon
   = $(5 - 2) \times 180° = 540°$ *(1 mark)*
   Sum of Amy's measurements:
   $91° + 118° + 108° + 77° + 150°$
   = 544° so Amy's measurements are not accurate. *(1 mark)*

Answers

6.

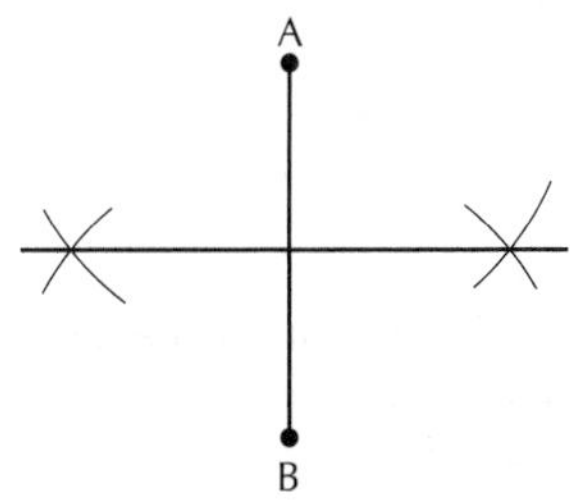

(2 marks available — 1 mark for correctly drawn construction arcs, 1 mark for a correct and accurate perpendicular bisector.)

7. $r^2 = 17^2 - 15^2$
$r^2 = 64$, so $r = 8$ cm.
$t^2 = 13^2 - 5^2$
$t^2 = 144$, so $t = 12$ cm.
So t is longer than r.
(2 marks for both lengths correct and a correct conclusion, otherwise 1 mark for working out one length correctly.)

Geometry and Measures: Test 6

1. A *(1 mark)*
2. C *(1 mark)*
3. 25 × 500 = 12 500 cm
= 125 m *(1 mark)*
40 ÷ 500 = 0.08 m
= 8 cm *(1 mark)*
4. E.g. Angle BCD = 180° – 68° = 112°
Angle ABE is corresponding to angle BCD so angle ABE = 112°.
(1 mark)
5. E.g.

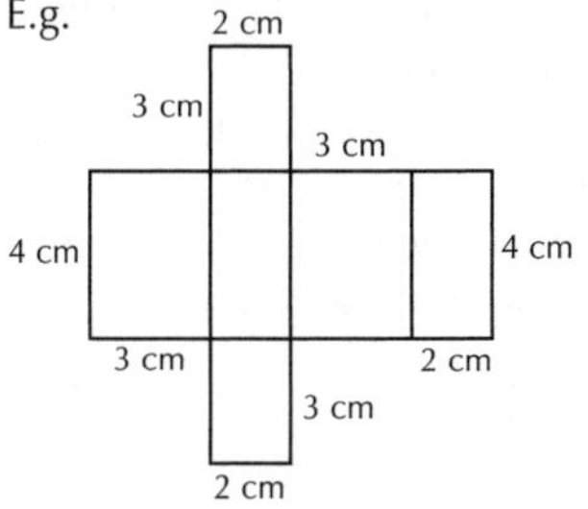

(2 marks available — 1 mark for drawing the net correctly, 1 mark for labelling it correctly.)

6. Area of circular face = $\pi \times 30^2$
= 2827.433... cm²
Circumference = $\pi \times 60$
= 188.495... cm
So area of curved rectangular face
= 188.495... × 50 = 9424.777... cm²
Total surface area
= (2 × 2827.433...) + 9424.777...
= 15 079.644... cm²
= 15 100 cm² (3 s.f.)
(3 marks available — 1 mark for finding the area of the circular faces, 1 mark for finding the area of the curved rectangular face, 1 mark for the correct answer.)

Geometry and Measures: Test 7

1. A *(1 mark)*
2. C *(1 mark)*
3. (6 – 2) × 180° = 720°
(2 marks available — 1 mark for using the correct formula, 1 mark for the correct answer.)
4. Area of plastic = 10 × 9 = 90 cm²
Radius of circle = 7 ÷ 2 = 3.5 cm
Area of circle = 38.4845... cm²
Area of remaining plastic
= 90 – 38.4845...
= 51.5154... = 51.5 cm² (3 s.f.)
(2 marks available — 1 mark for finding the area of the circle, 1 mark for the correct answer.)
5. 6 ÷ 6 = 1, so 1 domino will fit in the width of the box.
33 ÷ 3 = 11, so 11 dominoes will fit in the length of the box.
2.5 ÷ 0.5 = 5, so 5 dominoes will fit in the height of the box.
So there are a total of:
1 × 11 × 5 = 55 dominoes
(2 marks available — 1 mark for a correct method, 1 mark for the correct answer.)
6. $\tan x = \frac{2.4}{20}$
$x = \tan^{-1}(0.12) = 6.8427... = 6.8°$
(2 marks available — 1 mark for a correct method, 1 mark for the correct answer.)

BONUS BRAINTEASER

The ball travels a horizontal distance of 15 m and rises a total of 2.4 – 1 = 1.4 m.
Let x be the angle the ball travels.
$\tan x = \frac{1.4}{15}$
$x = \tan^{-1}\left(\frac{1.4}{15}\right) = 5.3321...$
$= 5.3°$ (1 d.p.)

Geometry and Measures: Test 8

1. B *(1 mark)*
2. A *(1 mark)*
3.

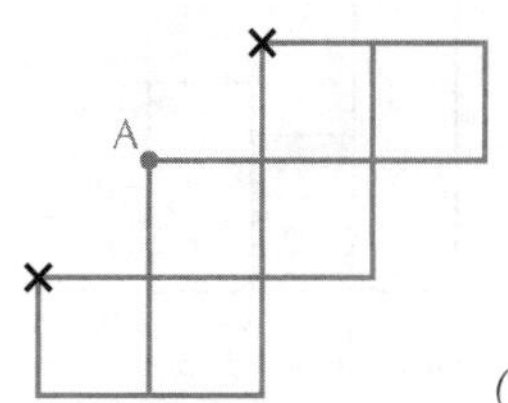

(1 mark)

4. Area = $\pi \times 1.2^2$
= 4.5238... cm²
= 4.52 cm² (3 s.f.) *(1 mark)*
1 m = 100 cm
Volume = 4.5238... × 100
= 452.3893... cm³
= 452 cm³ (3 s.f.) *(1 mark)*
5. Use Pythagoras' Theorem to find the height of the pole:
$30^2 - 10^2 = 800$ *(1 mark)*
$\sqrt{800} = 28.2842...$
= 28.28 m (2 d.p.) *(1 mark)*
6. cos (angle DAC) = $\frac{9}{12}$
angle DAC = $\cos^{-1}\left(\frac{9}{12}\right)$
= 41.4096...° *(1 mark)*
sin (angle BAC) = $\frac{8}{12}$
angle BAC = $\sin^{-1}\left(\frac{8}{12}\right)$
= 41.8103...° *(1 mark)*
So angle DAB
= 41.4096...° + 41.8103...°
= 83.2199...°
= 83° (to the nearest whole number)
(1 mark)

Answers

Probability and Statistics: Test 1

1. B *(1 mark)*
2. C *(1 mark)*
3. Range = 15 – 6 = 9 *(1 mark)*
4. $\frac{3}{8}$ *(1 mark)*
   $\frac{3}{8} \times 200 = 75$ *(1 mark)*
5. 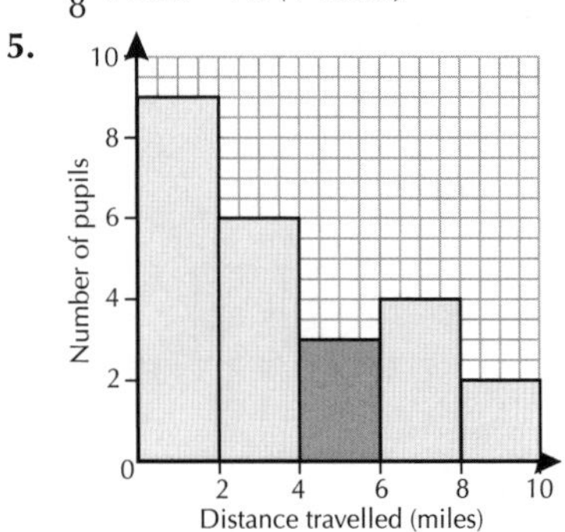

   (1 mark)
   4 + 2 = 6 pupils travel more than 6 miles *(1 mark)*
6. Probability of landing on purple
   $= \frac{3}{12} = \frac{1}{4}$
   Probability of not landing on purple
   $= 1 - \frac{1}{4} = \frac{3}{4}$ *(1 mark)*
7. Put the data in order:
   17, 18, 18, 21, 22, 25,
   26, 26, 28, 29, 31, 32
   The median is halfway between the 6th and 7th values: *(1 mark)*
   (25 + 26) ÷ 2 = 25.5 seconds
   (1 mark)

Probability and Statistics: Test 2

1. A *(1 mark)*
2. B *(1 mark)*
3. 4 out of 16 options, so probability of picking the same colour
   $= \frac{4}{16} = \frac{1}{4}$ *(1 mark)*
4. Claire, Evie, Luke, Mohammed.
   Claire, Evie, Mohammed, Luke.
   Claire, Luke, Evie, Mohammed.
   Claire, Mohammed, Evie, Luke.
   (1 mark)
5. E.g.
   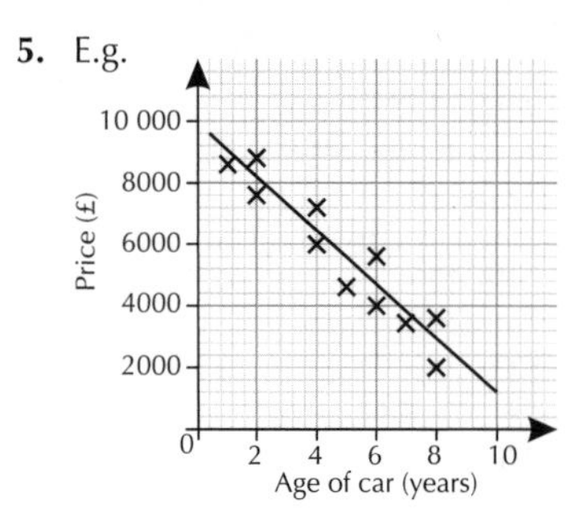

   (1 mark)
   Strong negative correlation
   (1 mark)
   £2000 (allow £1800 to £2200)
   (1 mark)
6. 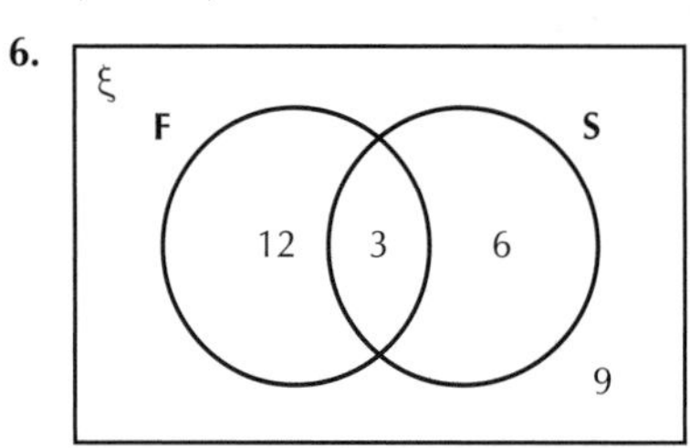

   (2 marks for all values filled in correctly, otherwise 1 mark for two or three values filled in correctly.)
   3 + 6 = 9 people have been to Spain, so the probability is $\frac{9}{30} = \frac{3}{10}$
   (1 mark)

BONUS BRAINTEASER

6 + 9 = 15 people haven't been to France, so the probability is $\frac{15}{30} = \frac{1}{2}$

Probability and Statistics: Test 3

1. B *(1 mark)*
2. A *(1 mark)*
3. E.g. The probability of a fair six-sided dice landing on a six is $\frac{1}{6}$, so the dice should land on a six $\frac{1}{6} \times 150 = 25$ times.
   25 is close to 27, so the dice does seem fair. *(1 mark)*
4. Multiplier = 360 ÷ 60 = 6
   Walk: 18 × 6 = 108°
   Car: 31 × 6 = 186°
   Cycle: 6 × 6 = 36°
   Train: 3 × 6 = 18°
   Other: 2 × 6 = 12°
   (2 marks for all 5 angles correct, otherwise 1 mark for working out correct multiplier.)
5. E.g. 64
   (1 mark — allow alternative answers if based on a sensible line of best fit)
6. 67 minutes *(1 mark)*
7. Modal age group = 25-29 *(1 mark)*
   There are 200 people, so the median is halfway between the 100th and 101st pieces of data. This value lies in the 30-34 age group, so the median age group is 30-34.
   (2 marks available — 2 marks for the correct answer, otherwise 1 mark for finding that the median is between the 100th and 101st values.)

Probability and Statistics: Test 4

1. C *(1 mark)*
2. A *(1 mark)*
3. Probability of picking an aniseed ball
   $= 1 - \frac{1}{5} - \frac{4}{15} = 1 - \frac{3}{15} - \frac{4}{15}$
   $= \frac{8}{15}$ *(1 mark)*
4. 360° ÷ 72° = 5
   15 × 5 = 75 people
   (2 marks available — 1 mark for a correct method, 1 mark for the correct answer.)
5. Relative frequency: 0.14, 0.07, 0.15, 0.13, 0.16, 0.12, 0.13, 0.1
   (2 marks for all 8 correct, otherwise 1 mark for at least 5 correct.)
6. Mid-interval value: 5, 15, 25, 35
   $f \times x$: 20, 120, 300, 210 (total = 650)
   Mean = 650 ÷ 30 = 21.666...
   = 21.67 cm (2 d.p.)
   (3 marks available — 3 marks for the correct answer, otherwise 1 mark for all mid-interval values correct and 1 mark for all $f \times x$ values correct.)

M3XP31

